CAGE AND AVIARY SERIES

THE
PEAFOWL
OF THE
WORLD

THE
PEAFOWL
OF THE
WORLD

JOSEF BERGMANN

Published by:
SAIGA PUBLISHING CO. LTD.
1 Royal Parade, Hindhead, Surrey GU26 6TD, England.

Typeset in Palatino VIP 12 on 14 point
by Inforum Ltd, Portsmouth.
Printed and bound by the Pitman
Press, Bath

SAIGA PUBLISHING CO. LTD.
1 Royal Parade, Hindhead, Surrey
GU23 6TD.

Dedication

This book is dedicated to all those who gain pleasure from the appreciation and study of nature and her many wonders. One of these must surely be the remarkable peafowl which we must consider as being one of the finest creatures on our earth.

Joseph Bergmann

Acknowledgements

We thank the various bodies, such as museums, who kindly gave permission to reproduce photographs from paintings in their possession. In particular, the following should be mentioned: The Metropolitan Museum of Art, New York, the Munich Art Gallery and the Rijksmuseum, Amsterdam.

I am grateful to various artists and authors whose work was used in the preparation of this book.

Photographs were produced either by myself or by other photographers, including Gerhard Gronfield and Toni Angermayer.

Contents

	Page
Acknowledgements	vi
Monochrome Illustrations List	viii
Coloured Illustrations List	ix
PART I History of the Peafowl	1
PART II A General Description	13
PART III The Different Species	27
PART IV Management of Peafowl	49
PART V Peafowl in Art	67
Index	94
Bibliography	99

Monochrome Illustrations

Figure		Page
1.1	Body Regions and Plumage Features	2
1.2	Peacock roosting in its natural habitat	4
1.3	Peafowl often adorned the grounds of large mansions	5
2.1	Peafowl compared with other Gallinaceous birds	14
2.2	The Peafowl in flight	21
2.3	Peacock-shooting in India	23
2.4	The striking train of the male peafowl	24
2.5	Peafowl egg	25
3.1	Distribution Map	28
3.2	The White Peafowl	37
3.3	Feather Formation and Pattern	45
3.4	Peacock Hybrid X Domestic Fowl	48
4.1	Peafowl may be allowed to roam in a garden or park	50
4.2	The Shed	53
4.3	The Aviary	55
4.4	Feeding Utensils	57
4.5	Transportation	63
4.6	Health and Happiness	65
5.1	*Peacocks* by Melchior d'Hondecoeter	68
5.2	*Dead Birds* by Jan Weenix	70
5.3	*Collection of Birds* by Frans Snyders	71
5.4	*The Peacocks* by Rembrandt van Ryn	72
5.5	*The Poultry House* by Carl Jutz	73
5.6	*Le Paon* by W.H. Freeman	82
5.7	*Le Paon* by Edouard Travies	83
5.8	*Group of Blue Peafowl* by T.W. Wood	85
5.9	*Green Peacock* by Edward J. Detmold	90

Coloured Illustrations

Plate   *Page*

1   Pair of Green Peafowl (*Pavo muticus*)   7
2   Group of Peafowl showing the different species   8
3   The Courtship Ritual   17
4   Stages in Plumage Growth   18
5   Blue or Indian Peafowl (*Pavo cristatus*)   31
6   *Top:* Black-winged Peafowl (*Pavo cristatus* mut. *nigripennis*)
        Bottom: Green Peafowl (*Pavo muticus*)   32
7   Green or Scaled Peafowl in their natural habitat   41
8   Family of Congo Peafowl (*Afropavo congensis*)   42
9   *Top:* Inside the Shed
        Bottom: The Aviary   59
10 Stages of growth in the young birds   60
11 *Pair of Peafowl* by the Japanese artist Maruyama Okyo   75
12 *Green Peacock* by Araki Kampo   76
13 *Peafowl* by Ludwig Reichenbach   81
14 *Peafowl* by Joseph Wolf   82
15 Peacock in Sèvres porcelain made for Ludwig II   89
16 Porcelain Peacock designed by Theodor Kärner   90

I

History of the
Peafowl

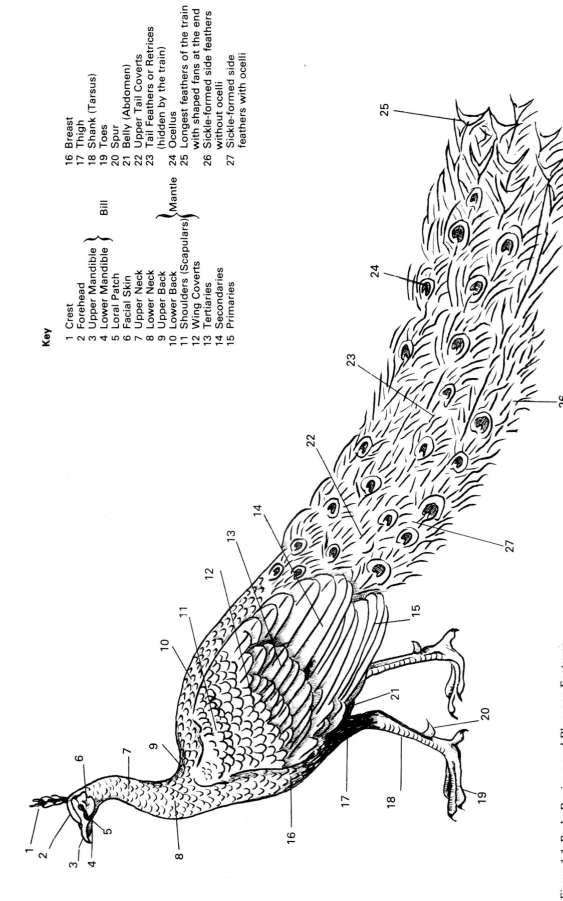

Key

1 Crest
2 Forehead
3 Upper Mandible ⎫
4 Lower Mandible ⎬ Bill
5 Loral Patch
6 Facial Skin
7 Upper Neck
8 Lower Neck
9 Upper Back
10 Lower Back ⎫
11 Shoulders (Scapulars) ⎬ Mantle
12 Wing Coverts
13 Tertiaries
14 Secondaries
15 Primaries
16 Breast
17 Thigh
18 Shank (Tarsus)
19 Toes
20 Spur
21 Belly (Abdomen)
22 Upper Tail Coverts
23 Tail Feathers or Retrices
   (hidden by the train)
24 Ocellus
25 Longest feathers of the train
   with shaped fans at the end
26 Sickle-formed side feathers
   without ocelli
27 Sickle-formed side
   feathers with ocelli

Figure 1.1 Body Regions and Plumage Features

History of the Peafowl

ANCIENT ORIGINS

OVER the centuries the peafowl has held a prominent place in the art, religion and general culture of many of the great civilizations. Often kept purely for its beauty and elegance, the peafowl must surely be the most colourful and spectacular member of the pheasant family, with the design and colour of the feathers attracting both artists and poets alike to use it as a symbol of power and beauty, as was the case in China and Japan.

The history of these birds is probably more varied and certainly more extensive than that of most other species, for it is mentioned even before those reports in the Bible of the Phoenicians bringing peafowl to King Solomon:

> "For the king had at sea a navy of Tharshish with the navy of Hiram: once in three years came the navy of Tharshish bringing gold, and silver, ivory, and apes, and peacocks."
> 1 Kings X, 22.

It is also reported that peafowl were imported by the Pharaohs of Egypt, where they figured prominently in the art and legends of that great empire.

There is a legend to be found in the Buddhist faith, that Buddha, the wise and gracious God, rode on the back of a peacock sitting in a lotus flower. Buddha was figured with four arms and with these he bestowed great happiness and good fortune on those who believed in his power. As easily as the peacock devours young snakes and harmful insects, so Buddha destroyed evils and unwholesome thoughts and gave his people's minds and souls new hope, wisdom, harmony and freedom. There are, to the present day, several fine paintings to be found in the museums of Japan depicting the Buddha — the Peacock-King — riding on a displaying peacock.

The peafowl held an important place in the legends and superstitions of the Far East for many centuries, but it was not until the conquests of Alexander the Great that the peafowl was introduced into Europe from its native home in India where it still remains a sacred bird. Taken from the Indus river, they were primarily to be found only in Greece where they were so admired that an order was passed to prevent anyone from putting them to death.

Once introduced to Greece, however, the peafowl spread throughout the Mediterranean countries and were known in England and France as early as the fourteenth century. For the Christians of that time the peacock was a symbol of the risen Jesus Christ and the image of these

3

birds was often to be found in paintings on the walls of the catacombs and in the mosaics lining the walls, floors and ceilings of the churches and meeting rooms.

It is said that Marco Polo first brought a drawing of *Pavo muticus* back from his journeys which was duly shown to the Pope. Thus, this rare bird became known to both the artists and scientists of that time and so reports and records may be found which date back to these years.

The appearance of the peafowl, and the many legends and superstitions surrounding this mysterious bird, has not always rendered it as a purely visible pleasure. Throughout the history of the Roman Empire large flocks of peafowl were kept for their meat which was considered a delicacy. Their brilliant plumage did not save them from slaughter and from dishes being prepared of their tongues, hearts and brains, as well as from their flesh. Due to their rarity and subsequent expense, no feast or banquet was considered complete without the peafowl which, when decorated with its colourful feathers, made a fitting centre-piece for the grandest of occasions.

The **Black-winged** peafowl was first mentioned by Latham in 1823; it appeared as a melanistic mutation living amongst normal flocks. **Green** peafowl were correctly described from living specimens by the author of the book *The Gardens and Menagerie of the Zoological Society*, Vol. II, *Birds*, in 1831. **Spalding** peafowl were also mentioned several times in the latter work, but a correct description of these fascinating birds is supplied here

Figure 1.2 Peacock roosting in its natural habitat

by the author who has kept them since 1963. A correct description of the **Congo** peafowl is also included, and, since these birds were only discovered in 1937, the author has tried to present clear and authentic illustrations of these birds as well as many other species.

Many writers have written on the peafowl and a few of the most important are as follows:*

Oliver Goldsmith: *A History of the Earth and Animated Nature*

"Our first peacocks were brought from the East Indies; and we are assured that they are still found in vast flocks, in a wild state, in the islands of Java and Ceylon. So beautiful a bird, and one esteemed such a delicacy at the tables of the luxurious, could not be permitted to continue long at liberty in its distant retreats. So early as the days of Solomon, we find in his navies, among the articles imported from the east, apes and peacocks. Ælian relates, that they were brought into Greece from some barbarous country, and were held in such high esteem among them, that a male and female were valued at about thirty pounds of our money. We are told also, that when Alexander was in India, he found them flying wild in vast numbers, on the banks of the river Hyarotis, and was so struck with their beauty, that he laid a severe fine and punishment on all who should kill or disturb them. Nor are we to be surprised at this, as the Greeks were so much struck with the beauty of this bird, when first brought among them, that every person paid a fixed price for seeing it; and several people came to Athens, from Lacedæmon and Thessaly, purely to satisfy their curiosity.

It was probably first introduced into the West merely on account of its beauty; but mankind, from contemplating its figure, soon came to think of serving it up for a different entertainment. Aufidius Hurco stands charged by Pliny with being the first who fatted up the peacock for the feast of the luxurious. Whatever there may be of delicacy in the flesh of a young peacock, it is certain an old one is very indifferent eating; nevertheless, there is no mention made of choosing the youngest; it is probably they were killed indiscriminately, the beauty of the feathers in some measure stimulating the appetite. Hortensius the orator, was the first who served them up at an entertainment at Rome; and

Figure 1.3 Peafowl often adorned the grounds of large mansions

* **A Bibliography is given in Appendix I**

Plate 1   Pair of Green Peafowl *(Pavo muticus)*

These birds have inspired legends and superstitions for many years and in certain countries, such as India, are held to be sacred. Their history is certainly more varied and extensive than that of most of other exotic species and dates back to the time of King Solomon.

(From an original watercolour by Josef Bergmann)

Pavo muticus

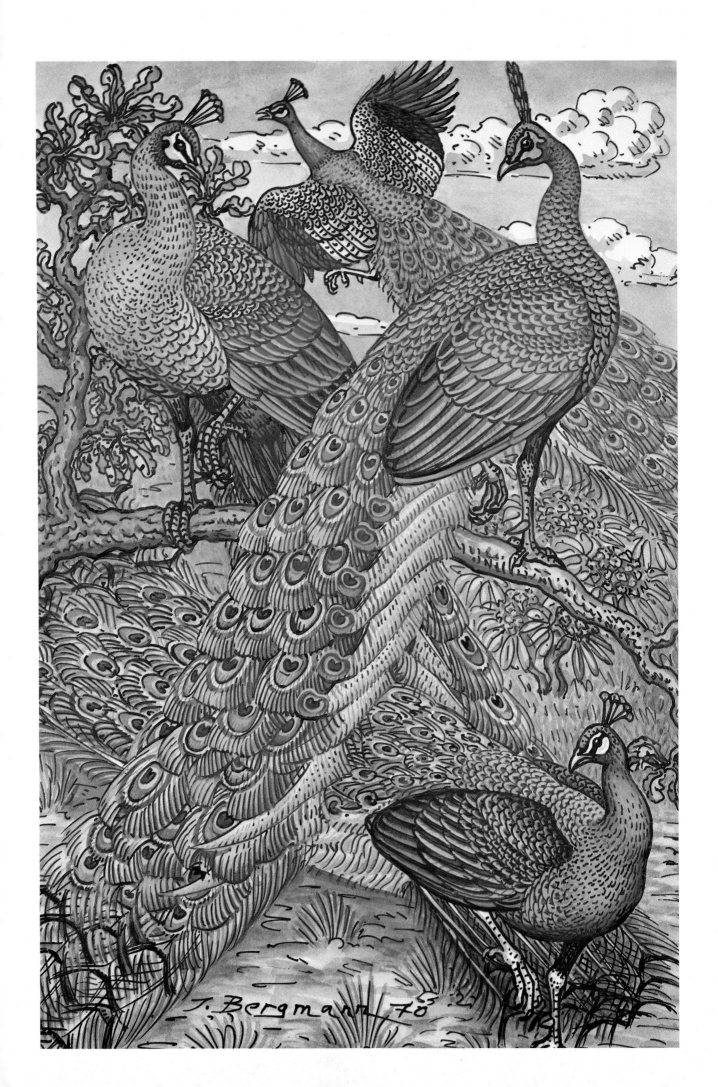

Blue or Indian Peacock (*Pavo cristatus*)

Spalding Peacock (hybrid)   Green Peacock (*Pavo muticus*)

Plate 2 Group of Peafowl showing the different species
(From an original watercolour by Josef Bergmann)

Black-winged Peacock (*Pavo cristatus* mut. *niggripennis*)

9

from that time they were considered as one of the greatest ornaments of every feast. Whether the Roman method of cookery, which was much higher than ours, might not have rendered them more palatable than we find them at present, I cannot tell; but certain it is, they talk of the peacock as being the first of viands.

Its fame for delicacy, however, did not continue very long: for we find in the times of Francis the First, that it was a custom to serve up peacocks at the tables of the great, with an intention not to be eaten, but only to be seen. Their manner was to strip off the skin; and then preparing the body with the warmest spices, they covered it up again in its former skin; with all its plumage in full display, and no way injured by the preparation. The bird thus prepared was often preserved for many years without corrupting; and it is asserted of the peacock's flesh, that it keeps longer unputrified than that of any other animal. To give a higher zest to these entertainments, on weddings particularly, they filled the bird's beak and throat with cotton and camphire,* which they set on fire, to amuse and delight the company. I do not know that the peacock is much used at our entertainments at present, except now and then at an alderman's dinner, or common-council feast, when our citizens resolve to be splendid; and even then it is never served with its cotton and camphire.''

W.B. Tegetmeier: *The Poultry Book*

"It is usually stated that but two species are known, — the common peacock, *Pavo cristatus*, and the Javan species, *Pavo muticus*. But Dr. Sclater has recently described, under the name of the black-winged peafowl, *Pavo nigripennis*, a third which seems perfectly distinct from the two former. The common Peafowl, *Pavo cristatus*, has been known from the earliest periods; we are informed that the navy of Solomon brought to him every three years peacocks from Tarshish, 1 Kings x. 22. Peafowls were known to the Greeks, and largely bred by the Romans. The bird in its wild state is a native of the peninsula of India, the Himalayan mountains, up to a height of several thousand feet, the jungles in the salt range of the Punjaub, and the island of Ceylon. Jerdon, in his admirable work, thus describes it:

'Male with the head, neck and breast rich purple, with gold and green reflections; back green, the feathers scale-like, with coppery edges; the wings with the inner coverts, including the shoulder, white, striated with black; the middle coverts deep blue; the primaries and tail chesnut; abdomen and vent black; the train chiefly green, beautifully ocellated; the thigh coverts yellowish grey; head with a crest of about twenty-four feathers, only webbed at the tip, and green with blue and gold reflections. Bill horny brown; orbits naked whitish; the irides of dark brown; legs horny brown. Length to the end of the true tail, 3½ to 4 feet; wing 18 inches; tail 24; the long train sometimes measures 4½ feet, and even more.

The female or Peahen is chesnut brown, the upper plumage light hair-brown, with faint wavings, increased on the upper tail-coverts; quills brown; some of the wing coverts mottled dusky and whitish; tail deep brown with whitish tips; chin and throat white; breast as the neck; abdomen white, with the lower parts and under tail-coverts brown.

Length 38 to 40 inches; wing 16; tail 14. The crest is shorter and duller in its tint than in the male.

The Peafowl is too well known to require a more ample description. It inhabits the whole of India Proper, being replaced in Assam and the countries to the East by another species. It frequents forests, and jungly places, more especially delighting in hilly and mountainous districts; and, in the more open and level country, wooded ravines and river banks are its never-failing resort. It comes forth to the open glades and fields to feed in the morning and evening, retiring to the jungles for shelter during the heat of the day, and roosting at night on high trees. It ascends the Neilgherry and other mountain regions in Southern India, to 6,000 feet or so of elevation, but it does not ascend the Himalayas, at all events in Sikim, beyond 2,000 feet. In many part of the country it is almost domesticated, entering villages and roosting on the huts; and it is venerated by the natives in many districts. Many Hindoo temples have large flocks of them; indeed, shooting it is forbidden in some Hindoo states. The Peafowl breeds, according to the locality, from April till October, generally in Southern India towards the close of the rains, laying from 4 to 8 or 9 eggs in some sequestered spot. The Peacock during the courting season raises his tail vertically, and with it of course the lengthened train, spreading it out and strutting about to captivate the hen birds; and he has the power of clattering the feathers in a most curious manner.

---

* Editorial Note: "Camphire" is a variation of the word camphor which refers to a whitish translucent, crystalline, volatile substance with aromatic smell and bitter taste. The variation used here is now obsolete.

It is a beautiful sight to come suddenly on twenty or thirty Peafowl, the males displaying their gorgeous trains, and strutting about in all the pomp of pride before the gratified females. The train of course increases in length for many years at each successive moult, but it appears to be shed very irregularly.

Though it cannot be said to be a favourite game with sportsmen in India, few can resist a shot at a fine peacock whirring past when hunting for small game: yet pea-chicks are well worth a morning's shikar for the table, and a plump young peahen, if kept for two or three days, is really excellent. An old peacock is only fit to make soup of. A bird merely winged will often escape by the fleetness of its running. They generally roost on particular trees, and by going early or late to this place, they can readily be shot.

Peafowl are easily caught in snares, common hair-nooses, and are generally brought in alive, for sale in numbers, in those districts where they abound. In confinement they will destroy snakes and other reptiles, and in their wild state feed much on various insects and grubs, also on flower buds and young shoots, as well as on grain."

Lewis Wright: *Illustrated Book of Poultry*

"If the references to the peacock in the two parallel passages of Scripture, 1 Kings x. 22 and 2 Chron. ix. 21, are correct translations of the Hebrew word *Tukiyyim*, the bird has been known from the earliest times; and the decision of this question invests the Pea-fowl with an historical and geographical interest, greater perhaps than can be attached to any other bird, since upon it almost exclusively depends the further question as to the aim and extent of Solomon's voyages, and the locality of the Ophir to which in other places they are said to have been directed. That Ophir is identical with the country from which the various products named in these verses were obtained may almost be assumed, and as every one of these except the *Tukiyyim* could have been obtained from either Arabia, Africa, or India, the whole of this interesting question almost entirely depends upon what creature is meant by the Hebrew word. Apart from this all is doubtful, for even the extraordinary supposition (made to account for the length of the three years' voyage) that the fleet went southward from the Red Sea, rounded the Cape of Good Hope, and finally reached Spain, is not so wild as may appear when taken in conjunction with the statement of Herodotus, that the King of Egypt known in Scripture as Pharaoh Necho despatched vessels manned by Phœnicians three centuries later, which performed this very voyage. It is true Herodotus himself discredits this account; but as he does so solely on the ground that these mariners affirmed "they had the sun on their right hand" after having sailed round Libya, which he considered ridiculous "romancing", whereas we now know what the old astronomers were ignorant of, that this was *exactly what would happen* after crossing the Line, his very objection makes the truth of the narrative almost absolutely certain; and it may be argued with much plausibility, that Necho probably directed his voyage from reports of the former successful expeditions by Solomon three hundred years before.

In that case, however, it is most difficult to conceive what can be intended by the *Tukiyyim*. The word, it is true, has been supposed by Hebrew scholars to be derived from a foreign root, signifying "tufted," or "crested;" and although the peacock is crested, the crest is far from being so conspicuous a characteristic as the gorgeous plumes. Hence a crested parrot has been conjectured; but it does not appear that the ancients were acquainted with parrots, and much less with any crested parrot, till long after. In fact parrots do not appear to have been known till the time of Alexander, and even then the varieties we find traces of were non-crested birds imported from Ceylon. The pheasant has also been supposed, but the only species of this genus known to the ancients was also without crest; and if we are to go eastward for a crested species, we may much better accept the peacock at once. In fact, supposing an African Ophir at all, the only bird which could possibly satisfy such a derivation of *Tukiyyim*, would be one we have never yet seen suggested by any biblical scholar — the Guinea fowl, of which the crest of feathers on some varieties, and the bony casque on others, might be suggested as giving rise to it. This indeed offers, in our opinion, the only tenable alternative supposing the peacock to be rejected; but it is open to the grave and, we think, fatal objection, that there is nothing in this fowl — singular in many respects at it is — to account for its being mentioned in such a special manner, while its abundance in Abyssinia would make a three years' voyage quite needless to obtain as many specimens as could be desired.

If we consider the Peacock to be really meant, however, all difficulties appear to vanish. There are some other indications which may point to Ophir being in the East Indies; as, for instance, that the natives of Malacca still call their gold mines *ophirs* (De Poivre); but one of the most singular, and more connected with our immediate subject, is that in Malabar the peacock is still called *Togei*, and in one of the Indian dialects, *Tikki*, which may furnish a very probable derivation for the word *Tukiyyim*. That such a gorgeous bird as the peacock should be sought for and valued by a magnificent monarch like Solomon, who is also expressly stated to have taken special interest in and had special knowledge of natural history, is highly probable; and it is equally so that a writer who had never seen anything approaching such plumage should deem it worthy of special mention: while we do know that the bird was at a later age eagerly sought, dedicated to Juno, and first bred in captivity in her temple at Samos. If any connection with "crest" or "tuft" be also sought in the name, and the crest of the bird itself be— as we certainly think it is— insufficient to account for it, we may suppose that the splendid tail *carried erect* may be referred to; or even, as it is well known that the plumes were eagerly sought for to be used in head-dresses, that the derivation may be thus explained; for it is to be remembered that the root-word being exotic, the exact signification is now difficult to ascertain. Some Indian region would supply just the distance needed for a three years' voyage in those days; and on all these and other grounds, it is now considered far the most probable that Solomon really was nearly or quite the first to import this beautiful bird from the East, and that some southern region of the Indies— it might be India itself, or Malacca, or perhaps Ceylon— was the locality from which they and the other precious products enumerated were procured.

The few lines we have devoted to this curious subject will hardly be considered as wasted, if it be remembered that such conclusions— supposing them to be correct— point to Solomon as *the first importer of fancy poultry* and, singularly enough, from the very same region whence the most striking of our own more modern varieties have been obtained. So curious an idea may be smiled at, and perhaps be even classed with the familiar assumption regarding the same monarch being "the first Freemason"; but in this case we have at least a fair amount of solid evidence in favour of such an honour and antiquity for our noble craft."

II

A General Description

Figure 2.1 Peafowl compared with other Gallinaceous birds – they are indeed the most splendid of this family

A General Description

PEAFOWL IN THE WILD

T HE **Asiatic** peafowl is found exclusively in Eastern Asia where its natural haunts cover a wide range of land, spreading throughout the whole of India and the adjacent islands, and also extending into parts of China. The **Congo** peafowl has a less extensive habitat, being found mainly in the dense forests of South Western Zaire.

The habitat of the wild peafowl varies a great deal. They are to be found living in both scrub areas and dense forests as well as in more open country. They are seldom seen above 3,000 feet due to their need and liking for water, although it has been found that they can stand cold weather and need little protection from the elements. The birds are often found in flocks around the banks of rivers, often near to the native settlements, one male usually being surrounded by two to five females.

In their natural state, peafowl feed mainly on insects, seeds, grasses and other small plants, and also small reptiles. Young cobras are another addition to their varied diet and because of this they are protected in many parts of India by the Hindus.

THE COURTSHIP OF THE PEAFOWL

In the pairing season rival males display before their desired mates and carry out a courtship ritual similar to that of other game birds. The cocks raise their impressive train, thereby forming a fan and revealing some 150 strikingly coloured "eyes" or ocelli. This display is often accompanied by a rattling of the quills and a shrill cry, as the peacocks dance back and forth, with train erect, in order to attract the attention of the hens. The cry of the male differs among the different varieties: the Blue Indian peafowl having a loud and harsh "hiau", whilst the Green varieties of Asia cry "pavo" or "hiao" less frequently and in a deeper and quieter tone than that of the Blue.

The mating period of the European peafowl lasts from approximately April to July. During this time the peahen may also be seen to display by spreading and raising her upper tail coverts and retrices. Young chicks sometimes imitate the courtship display of the parent birds in order to impress each other. The ritual of the peacock need not be confined to the mating season alone — peacocks have been seen to show-off in this manner all the year round, often when no female is even present.

The Congo peacock displays in the same manner, although it lacks the

15

Plate 3 The Courtship Ritual

Top: As part of the courtship ritual the peacocks raise their impassive trains in an effort to attract the hens. This display is often accompanied by a rattling of the quills and a shrill cry.

Bottom: The colourful train hides the real tail feather or retrices which are not nearly so striking as their coverts, being blackish-brown in colour.

Plate 4 Stages in Plumage Growth

    A   Year-old Black-winged peacock
    B   Year-old Blue peacock, displaying
    C   Six-week old Spalding chick
    D   Spalding peahen
    E   Three-week old Blue chick
    F   Pied/Black-winged hybrid peacock

(From an original watercolour by Josef Bergmann)

long train of the other male varieties. However, most of this bird's plumage shows a metallic gloss and its display is still impressive.

THE NEST

The birds, though preferring to roost in high trees, where they hold a commanding view of the surrounding terrain and any approaching danger, seek their food and construct their nesting place on the ground. The clutch, containing numerous eggs (eight to ten in number) of a brownish colour, is laid on the ground in a well-concealed place— often amongst close brushwood or hidden by branches or high grass. The nest itself is practically non-existent, the eggs being laid virtually on the ground, sometimes with sticks, twigs, dried grasses and leaves provided by the peahen to give a rough protection.

After hatching, both sexes are similar in appearance and it is not until the third year that the brilliant plumage of the male bird becomes fully developed.

In their wild state the main enemies of the peafowl are the larger members of the cat family; for example, the tiger and leopard. The loud and piercing cries of the birds serve a dual purpose as they warn other animals, besides those of their own kind, of any approacing predators such as wild dogs, martens or pythons. When attacked, peafowl will run at a suprising speed in order to escape their enemies, even through scrub or other dense vegetation, rather than taking flight as a means of escape.

Here follows a description of the peafowl in its wild state which appeared in *The Poultry Book* by Tegetmeier (*ibid*):

"A series of admirable articles on the Game birds of India in *The Field*, under the *nom-de-plume* of "Ornithognomon", graphically described the habits of these birds in their wild state:—

"In the months of December and January the temperature in the forests of Central India, especially in the valleys, is very low, the cold, from sudden evaporation, being intense at sunrise. The peafowl in the forests may be observed at such times still roosting, long after the sun has risen above the horizon. As the mist rises off the valleys, and gathering into little clouds, goes rolling up the hill-sides till lost in the ethereal blue, the peafowl descend from their perches on some huge seemul or saul tree, and threading their way in silence through the underwood, emerge into the fields, and make sad havoc with the chunna, oorid (both vetches), wheat, or rice. When sated they retire into the neighbouring thin jungle, and there preen themselves, and dry their bedewed plumage in the sun. The cock stands on a mound, or a fallen trunk, and sends forth his well-known cry, 'pehaun — pehaun,' which is soon answered from other parts of the forest. The hens ramble about, or lie down dusting their plumage; and so they pass the early hours while the air is still cool, and hundreds of little birds are flitting and chirruping about the scarlet blossoms of the 'polâs' or the 'seemul.' As the sun rises and the dewy sparkle on the foliage dries up, the air becomes hot and still, the feathered songsters vanish into shady nooks, and our friends the peafowl depart silently into the coolest depths of the forest, to some little sandy stream canopied by verdant boughs, or to thick beds of reeds and grass, or dense thorny brakes overshadowed by mossy rocks, where, though the sun blaze over the open country, the green shades are cool, and the silence of repose unbroken, though the shrill cry of the cicada may be heard ringing faintly through the wood. There are spots in these saul forests which, for luxurious coolness during the sultriest weather, rival the most elaborately devised recesses of the Alhambra, or the tinkling fountains and rose bowers of Isphahan — the paradise of the old Persian — and the wilder denizens of the woods show no small discernment in selecting them. Many a delightful dreamy hour I have passed in some such delicious spot, watching the little crystal streamlet at my feet,

Figure 2.2 The Peafowl in flight. Rarely do they take to the air as a means of escape; preferring to run through the undergrowth

(*Courtesy:* Gerhard Gronefeld)

lazily scanning the endless variety of unknown plants, flowers, ferns, fungi, and mosses scattered around, or following the movements of some honeysucker, as the tiny feathered jewel, emboldened by the silence, displayed his brilliant plumage scarce a yard from my admiring eyes. In such lovely retreats one might cheat the hot hours of noon, and rob them of their discomfort; but, alas! these are the spots where lurks malaria, and, moreover, where one may be very apt to intrude on the privacy of some misanthropic tiger! The fact that where peafowl abound tigers are very likely to be met with is well known to Indian sportsmen, and is confidently believed by the natives themselves.

These birds cease to congregate soon after the crops are off the ground. The pairing season is in the early part of the hot weather. The peacock has then assumed his full train, that is, the longest or last rows of his upper tail coverts, which he displays of a morning, strutting about before his wives. These strange gestures, which the natives gravely denominate the peacock's *nautch*, or dance, are very similar to those of a turkey cock, and accompanied by an occasional odd shiver of the quills, produced apparently by a convulsive jerk of the abdomen."

THE PEAFOWL AS SPORT

In their wild state peafowl were once shot as sport, and also destroyed in the same manner as vermin due to their large numbers and the deafening sound of their cries. In his *Illustrated Book of Poultry*, Lewis Wright covers this topic and an extract is included below:

"In some parts of India peacock-shooting is a recognised sport; while in others, and in some parts of Ceylon, the birds are so plentiful as to be cared little about. Thus Sir Emerson Tennant writes that, 'in Ceylon, as we emerge from the deep shade and approach the park-like openings on the verge of the low country, numbers of pea-fowl are to be found, either feeding on the seeds and fallen nuts among the long grass, or sunning themselves on the branches of the surrounding trees. Nothing to be met with in English demesnes can give an adequate idea of the size and magnificence of this matchless bird when seen in its native solitudes. Here he generally selects some projecting branch, from which his plumage may hang free of the foliage; and if there be a dead and leafless bough he is certain to choose it for his resting-place, whence he droops his wings and spreads his gorgeous train in the morning sun to drive off the damps and dews of night. In some of the unfrequented portions of the eastern province, to which Europeans rarely resort, and where the pea-fowl are unmolested by the natives, their number is so extraordinary that, regarded as game, it ceases to be sport to destroy them; and their cries at early dawn are so tumultuous and incessant as to banish sleep and amount to an actual inconvenience. Colonel Williamson has described peacock-shooting in India itself in somewhat similar terms. 'About the passes in the Jungleterry districts,' he writes, 'I have seen such quantities of pea-fowl as have absolutely surprised me. Whole woods were covered with their beautiful plumage, to which a rising sun imparted additional brilliancy. The small patches of plain among the long grass, most of them cultivated, and with mustard then in bloom, which induced the birds to feed, added beauty to the scene; and I speak within bounds when I assert that there could not be less than twelve or fifteen hundred pea-fowl of various sizes within sight of the spot where I stood for nearly an hour.' He says it is easy enough to get a shot in the jungle, but when the birds flocked together to the number of forty of fifty it was more difficult, as they run very fast, and prefer this method of escape to taking wing. He doubts, in fact, if a slow dog could raise them at all. He says they fly heavily, and generally give an easy shot when once raised; but if only winged will speedily recover themselves, and in nine cases out of ten escape on foot, owing to their swiftness. He also mentions the curious fact that wherever peacocks abound the tiger is generally found also more near than convenient, so that peacock-shooting is by no means devoid of danger."

GENERAL CHARACTERISTICS OF THE PEAFOWL

The peafowl, belonging to the genus *Pavo*, are, indeed, the largest of the gallinaceous birds. A general description of their characteristics is discussed below, but it must be remembered that there is much variation

Figure 2.3 Peacock-shooting in India. These birds were once destroyed as vermin

(From an old print)

between the different species and so deviations from the general rule will be found.

Peafowl may be distinguished from other birds belonging to the order **Galliformes**, by the erect crest which adorns the head of both the male and female. This crest is supported by a small head and a long, slender neck. The body and wings of both sexes are rounded, with most of the plumage showing metallic colours, although this is more pronounced in the male.

The males have a long train, composed of some 220 upper tail coverts which hide the 20 graduated retrices, or tail feathers. The latter are a dull greyish brown, as is the underside of the train, and it is only on the upper side that the brilliant metallic feathers with their striking design appear. The females have no train and also lack the spurs that may be seen on the males.

Figure 2.4 The striking train of the male peafowl

THE YOUNG

As already stated, the young, on hatching, are alike in appearance, but some weeks after hatching the two may be distinguished by reason of a difference in the colour of the primaries of the sexes— the males being a clear, light brown/cinnamon whilst the young females are a dull brown, mottled with dark brown or black.

After the first year the males can be easily detected by the brighter plumage that appears on their head, neck and breast. However, full adult plumage is not gained until the third year.

Tegetmeier (*ibid*), a famous naturalist, described the nesting habits of the peafowl and the appearance of the young in the following terms:

> "The hen lays in Central India during June and July. The eggs, amounting sometimes to eight or ten, are laid on the bare ground, generally under a thicket, in the deepest and most secluded part of the jungle; they are of a dull brownish white, about 2¾ inches in length, and 2¼ in breadth. The chicks run about as soon as hatched. They are at first covered with down, and in about a week begin to assume their first feathers, which are of a dull dark brown above and paler below, in both sexes, the sides of the head whitish, with a dark band through the eye. The cock remains for a year or eighteen months of the same colour as the hen, and does not assume the long tail coverts till the third year; these fall off when moulting in the rains, and the new coverts remain short till about November or December, when the last rows elongate rapidly."

The chicks are soon strong enough to make use of their legs and wings and can be seen following their mother and even fluttering around on the lower branches of the trees in the first few weeks after hatching. When at rest the young are protected under the mother's wing or tail.

Figure 2.5 Peafowl egg – brownish in colour and approximately the size of a goose egg

THE MOULT

In or around July the moulting season begins. The cocks lose their entire train, as well as the retrices and wing feathers. The new plumage commences growth in about October or November with the train reaching its full length and splendour in the following April or May.

Both the male and female moult very fast, although the growth of the new feathers takes many months. During the period of the moult the birds appear to suffer more than other birds and tend to seek seclusion until their feathers have returned.

III

The Different Species

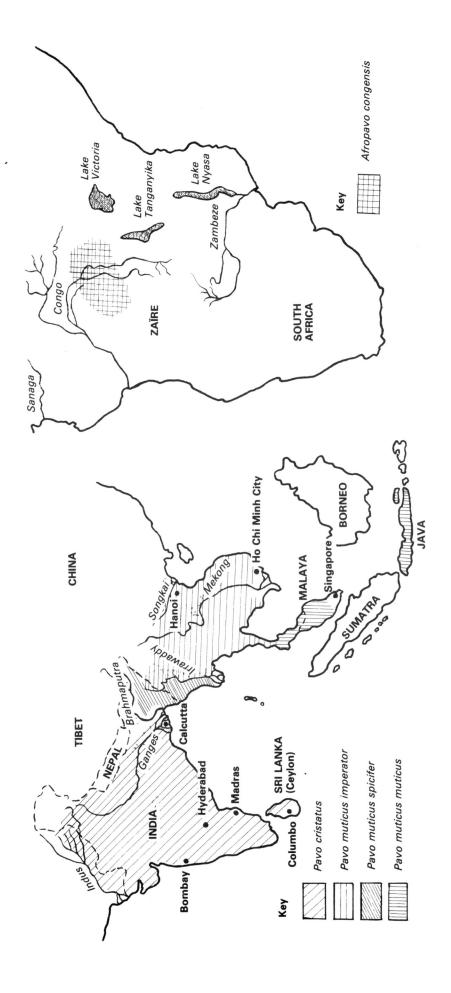

Figure 3.1 Distribution map

Key *Afropavo congensis*

Lake Victoria
Lake Tanganyika
Lake Nyasa
Zambeze
Congo
ZAÏRE
SOUTH AFRICA
Sanaga

CHINA
TIBET
NEPAL
Brahmaputra
Indus
Ganges
INDIA
Bombay
Hyderabad
Madras
Calcutta
SRI LANKA (Ceylon)
Columbo
Irrawaddy
Songkai
Hanoi
Mekong
Ho Chi Minh City
MALAYA
Singapore
BORNEO
SUMATRA
JAVA

Key
Pavo cristatus
Pavo muticus imperator
Pavo muticus spicifer
Pavo muticus muticus

The Different Species

MAIN SPECIES AND VARIETIES

I T is necessary at this stage to summarize the main species and varieties, thus allowing the reader to see at a glance the main names before going on to study the descriptions of each bird in turn. The latter have been taken from the author's own birds and are aimed at presenting to the reader a true idea of the appearance of the different species. However, it must be remembered that the markings and colour of the birds are subject to much variation. This may be due to age, habitat or simply breeding and, therefore, variations in description may be found. The summary is as follows:

1. **Blue** or **Indian** peafowl (*Pavo cristatus*)
2. **Black-winged** peafowl (*Pavo cristatus* mut. *nigripennis*)
3. **White** peafowl (mutation)
4. **Pied** peafowl (hybrid)
5. **Green** or **Scaled** peafowl (*Pavo muticus*):
   (a) **Javanese Green** peafowl (*Pavo muticus muticus*)
   (b) **Indo-Chinese Green** peafowl (*Pavo muticus imperator*)
   (c) **Western Burmese Green** peafowl (*Pavo muticus spicifer*)
6. **Emerald** or **Spalding** peafowl (hybrid)
7. **Congo** peafowl (*Afropavo congensis*)

These are now examined in the following text with illustrations to supplement the descriptions.

THE BLUE OR INDIAN PEAFOWL
(Pavo cristatus)

Natural Distribution: most parts of India and Ceylon.

MALE

Crown   Fan-shaped crest a metallic blue with greenish-blue tips.
Head   Bright, glossy blue with a patch of bare facial skin around the eye which is white in colour.
Neck   Bright, glossy blue, changing from cobalt blue to a dark ultramarine on the lower part of the neck.
Breast   Ultramarine and cobalt blue, changing to black on the lower breast and a dark glossy green on the sides.
Belly (abdomen)   Dull grey.

29

Plate 5 Blue or Indian Peafowl *(Pavo cristatus)*

Found living naturally throughout most parts of India and Ceylon. The birds are often to be seen perching in trees, often one male accompanied by several females.

(From an original watercolour by Josef Bergmann)

Plate 6   *Top:* Black-winged peafowl (*Pavo cristatus* mut. *nigripennis*)
Bottom: Green peafowl (*Pavo muticus*)
(From an original watercolour by Josef Bergmann)

Thighs   Off-white.

Back   Golden, changing to green; each feather having a brown 'V' shaped patch which is narrowly edged with black.

Shoulders (scapulars)   Buff-white, irregularly mottled and barred with black.

Wing Coverts and **Tertiaries**   Also buff-white, irregularly barred and mottled with black. Outermost feathers blue-black.

Secondaries   Upper feathers having similar colouring to the tertiaries but being bluish black on the innermost feathers so showing as a dark stripe on the wing.

Primaries   Fulvous or cinnamon.

Tail   The upper tail coverts which form the train are made up of disintegrated metallic barbs which alter from a coppery-bronze through gold to a dark green. Many of these show the well known "eyes", or ocelli, which consist of a deep blue patch bordered by two broad rings. The first of these is a brilliant blue or green, the second a coppery-brown. Encircling the latter are two narrow rings of colour: firstly one of a golden-green and finally one of lilac. The longest thirty to forty train feathers end in a broad, black "V" shaped fan, the remainder of these being golden-green in colour. The sickle-formed side feathers, when erected, form a fine border at the sides of the main fan and are a glittering golden-green. These have a reduced "eye-spot". *

Bill   Horny grey.   **Legs** and **Feet**   Pale grey/white.

Total length   1.80–2.20 m (5.91–7.22 feet).

Length of Wing   49.5 cm (18.7 inches).

Length of Tail   1.40–1.60 m (4.59–5.25 feet).

Culmen (Upper mandible)   4.5 cm (1.77 inches).

Tarsus (Shank)   12–15 cm (4.72–5.91 inches).

Thigh   10 cm (3.94 inches).

Spur   2.5 cm (0.98 inches).

   The measurements for the tarsus quoted above take into account the difference between a domestic and a wild species of peafowl. The latter having the longer leg of the two and, therefore, a slightly taller appearance.

FEMALE

Crown   Green tips to the brown feathers.

Head   Brown with the face and chin being white.

Neck   Glossy bronze-green, some feathers having a buffy-grey border.

Breast   Upper breast glossy green, the feathers bordered with buff-grey; lower breast dark brown with broad buff-white borders to the feathers.

Belly   Pale greyish buff.

Thighs   Grey-brown mottled.

Back   Upper parts grey-brown.

Shoulders   Earthy brown marked with a paler brown, as are the

* The longest tail feathers have no "eye-spot".

tertiaries and **secondaries**.
Primaries   Chestnut bordered with a blackish-brown.
Tail   Retrices dark brown.
Bill and **Legs**   Horny brown.
Total length   95 cm (37.4 inches).
Wing   40 cm (15.75 inches).
Tail   35 cm (13.78 inches).
Culmen   4 cm (1.57 inches).
Tarsus of wild hen   12–13 cm (4.72–5.12 inches).

CHICKS

These are a buff colour on the underside and brown on the upper parts. The head and back are dark brown. The tips of the largest scapulars (shoulder feathers) and the wing coverts are white with a broad, subterminal black bar. The secondaries and retrices are boldly barred with black.

First Year Males show a blue neck and breast; the back is greyish, irregularly barred and mixed with metallic green. The plumage becomes like that of an adult in the third year.

BLACK-WINGED PEAFOWL
(*Pavo cristatus* mut. *nigripennis*)

Black-winged peafowl first appeared in England during the first half of the nineteenth century amongst flocks of normal and Pied peafowl.

MALE

Shoulders   Black fringed with dark green.
Wing Coverts   Black fringed with dark green, the outermost coverts being fringed with blue.
Primaries   Reddish-brown fringed with black.
Thighs   Black/dark brown.
   All other plumes like *cristatus*.

FEMALE

Head   Light rufous.
Neck   Upper neck white with some rufous markings; hind neck white barred with shining green; lower neck white, finely stippled with grey.
Breast   Creamy-white freckled with grey/brown.
Belly   Creamy-white.
Back   White, barred and mottled with dark brown.
Secondaries   Heavily marked with dark brown.
Primaries   Fulvous.

Tail   Tail coverts white with a dark brown line along the shaft. Retrices a dark greyish-brown.

CHICKS

Creamy-white, with the first year young being mottled with black. The neck and upper breast of the males becoming blue as they grow and moult.

WHITE PEAFOWL

This mutation is entirely white, as the plumage is devoid of any other pigment. The eyes are dark brown in colour; the bill and legs a creamy-white. Although lacking colour, their appearance is no less striking than that of the other species. The structure of the barbs of their feathers create an eye-catching design as can be seen from Figure 3.2.

White peafowl, in domesticity, should be kept on grass rather than bare earth as their feathers soon become soiled and give them a dull grey appearance. In habit they are no different from other species; they breed true.

PIED PEAFOWL

Pied peafowl are those whose plumage consists of irregular white patches of feathers replacing the normal colours. These patches vary in size and distribution.

This white factor may appear in all species and varieties and is generally thought to be an inherited characteristic. The incidence of a White peafowl among their ancestors is usually the basis for the appearance of this variety.

GREEN PEAFOWL
(Pavo muticus)

The green species of peafowl, also known as the **Scaled peafowl** because of its feather pattern, is found further to the east than its close relative, the Blue peafowl. Inhabiting Burma, Siam, Java and Indo-China as well as parts of Malaya, they avoid dense forests and open spaces preferring broken vegetation, river banks and grasslands.

The appearance of the Green peafowl differs in several ways from the Blue. The males are brighter in colour and have a crest composed of long barbed feathers which form a tuft, rather than the fan-like crest belonging to the Blue. The female also possesses a brighter plumage than her blue counterpart, although lacking the train and lustrous colouring of the green male.

Another factor affecting their appearance is the length of their legs or, more particularly, their tarsi. This appears to be longer in the green

Figure 3.2 The White Peafowl

species, so giving them a proud and slender stance which is less pronounced in *cristatus*.

In habits both species are similar, apart from the difference between the cry of each which is discussed in Chapter 2.

There are three main subspecies of the Green peafowl; these are examined below.

JAVENESE GREEN PEAFOWL
(Pavo muticus muticus)

Natural Distribution: This subspecies is distributed south from the Isthmus of Kra in Eastern Malaya, and is found particularly along the banks and around the area of the Pahang river. It is also found throughout Java.

MALE

Crown Metallic green and forming a tuft rather than a fan.

Head Dark blue-green with the bare facial skin being light blue near the eye with a bright yellow band underneath.

Neck Upper parts having the same dark blue-green colouring as the head. The feathers of the middle and lower neck have a greenish-black centre and a bronze border; this itself being fringed with black, giving a scaly appearance (hence the name Scaled peafowl).

Breast Similar feather formation to that of the neck but having a more coppery appearance, changing to emerald green on the lower parts.

Belly Very dark green/black.

Thighs Black.

Back Similar to *cristatus* but the feathers being of a different shape: smaller and more elongated, especially on the upper back. Although similar in general appearance to the Blue, they tend to be more brilliant and metallic in colour, changing from a rosy copper to green. Each feather has a dark green streak flanked by a bronze "V" shaped patch. The feather is fringed with a black line, approximately 2mm broad, thus giving the bird a scaled and darker green appearance than *cristatus* in this region.

Shoulders Blackish-brown, each feather broadly fringed with emerald green changing to a bronzy-gold.

Wing Coverts Bright, metallic emerald green and cobalt blue.

Tertiaries Blackish-brown, narrowly bordered with blue.

Secondaries Black with the outer webs being edged with a glossy dark green.

Primaries Light cinnamon, as are the coverts.

Tail The "eye" feathers of the train are similar to those of *cristatus* but the ocelli themselves are comparatively smaller on the upper third. The main difference between these markings in the birds is that in *muticus* the bronzy-brown ring surrounding the deep blue/green "heart spot" is fringed by a thin ring of blackish-brown, a similar ring of light golden-green and finally a very bright, broad ring (5 mm) of metallic lilac. In *cristatus* the gold-green line is broader (3 mm) and of a darker, duller gold. The lilac border is also duller, giving *muticus* a more striking appearance.

Bill Grey.
Legs Grey.
Total Length 2.40 m (7.87 feet).
Wing 50 cm (19.69 inches) or over.
Tail Train up to 1.60 m (5.25 feet). Retrices: 60 cm (23.62 inches).
Culmen 4.3 cm (1.69 inches).
Tarsus 16 cm (6.3 inches).
Thigh 15 cm (5.91 inches).

FEMALE

Similar, but lacking the brightness and extent of colour that is seen in the male. The neck feathers, scapulars and inner wing coverts are mottled with pale buff; the latter being bordered with green. The upper tail coverts are a bronzy-green barred with pale buff. Retrices are dark brown.

Total Length 100 cm (39.4 inches).
Wing 54 cm (17.72 inches).
Tail 45 cm (17.72 inches).
Culmen 4.2 cm (1.65 inches).
Tarsus 14 cm (5.51 inches).

CHICKS

Generally similar to the young of *cristatus* but being greyer in colour.

INDO-CHINESE PEAFOWL
(Pavo muticus imperator)

Natural Distribution: Indo-China, east from the Irrawaddy to Siam, Laos, Cambodia, and Vietnam.

MALE

Similar to *muticus* but with the neck and sides of the breast being more clearly fringed with bright golden-bronze, rather than olive-green. Scapulars are emerald green changing to blue, and lack the heavy gold colouring of *muticus*. In certain lights both subspecies appear to be bright, changing to dark, blue on the shoulders and wing coverts. They are then very difficult to distinguish.

Plate 7 Green or Scaled Peafowl in their natural habitat

These birds are found inhabiting Burma, Siam, Java and Indo-China as well as parts of Malaya. They are similar in habits to their close relative the Blue but tend to be brighter in colour and more striking in appearance.

(From an original watercolour by Josef Bergmann)

Plate 8 Family of Congo Peafowl *(Afropavo congensis)*

Discovered as recently as 1936, these birds are still considered a rarity and few are to be found in captivity. They differ markedly in appearance from the other peafowl; the males lacking the distinctive train and brilliant plumage of other species.

(From an original watercolour by Josef Bergmann)

FEMALE

Similar again to *muticus* but having more buff and less green colouring in the breast feathers.

BURMESE GREEN PEAFOWL
(*Pavo muticus spicifer*)

Natural Distribution: From Western Burma to the Irrawaddy. Has died out in parts of India and Pakistan where formerly it could be found. In other parts, such as the Chittagong valley, it is very scarce.

MALE

Much duller than the other subspecies. The borders of the neck and upper breast feathers are dull grey in colour, and lack the orange-bronze colouring of the other peafowl.

The shoulders are blackish-brown with the feathers having a narrow band of metallic blue or green at their edge. The remaining plumage is generally similar to the other subspecies of the Green peafowl.

FEMALE

Duller and bluer in colour than the other peahens. The upper parts showing larger areas of black-brown.

SPALDING OR EMERALD PEAFOWL

These are hybrids produced from a cross between either *muticus* and *cristatus* or *muticus* and *nigripennis*. They represent, in a certain sense, the finest and most decorative peafowl of all. They appear to have longer legs than the domesticated *cristatus* which gives them the proud and slender appearance of *muticus*.

MALE

Crown Similar to *cristatus* but more compressed and being of a brighter blue in colour.

Head Facial skin has the same form as *muticus* but it is white instead of blue around the eye, with a small yellow band on the lower part of the face.

Neck and **Breast** Bright emerald green with an iridescent quality which causes the feathers to appear dark green or blue in certain lights and positions.

Back Golden and green, with 'V' shaped green-bronze central patches. Each feather is fringed with a black border. This feather pattern and depth of colour represents the finest of its kind among the peafowl.

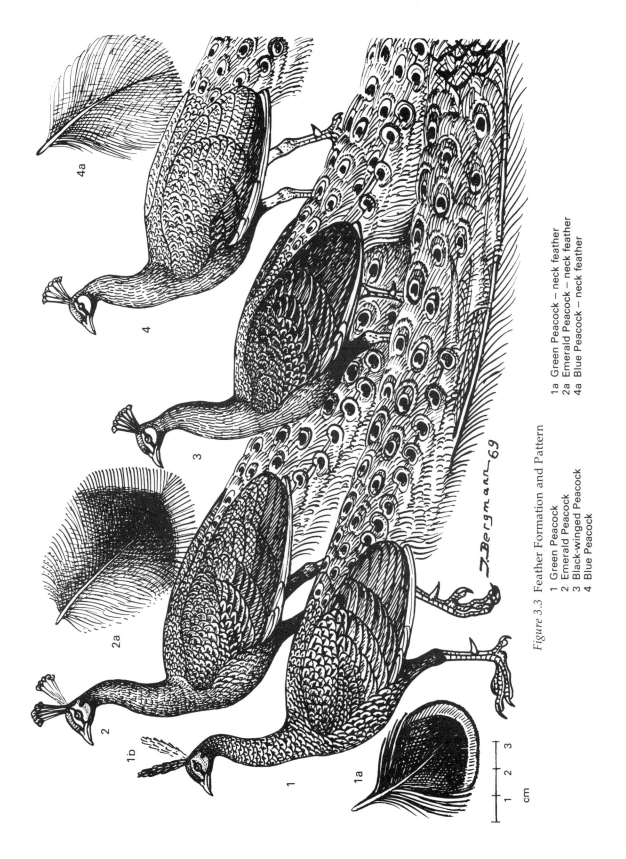

Figure 3.3 Feather Formation and Pattern

1 Green Peacock	1a Green Peacock – neck feather
2 Emerald Peacock	2a Emerald Peacock – neck feather
3 Black-winged Peacock	4a Blue Peacock – neck feather
4 Blue Peacock	

Shoulders and **Wings**   Similar to *muticus* but with the upper wing coverts and secondaries being a grey-brown mottled and barred with blackish-brown. These parts are darker in colour if the bird is a cross between *nigripennis* and *muticus*.

Tail   Similar to both *muticus* and *cristatus*. The golden-green ring of the ocelli being broader than that of *muticus*, but narrower than *cristatus*. The lilac border is bright and broad, as in *muticus*.

Total Length   Up to 2.30 m (7.55 feet).

Tail   1.60 m (5.25 feet).

FEMALE

Crown   Bright blue/green as in the male.

Neck   Bright emerald green with the underparts fringed with grey. This, however, is less obvious than in *cristatus*.

Breast   Blackish-green, each feather fringed with an orangey-brown.

Wings   Dark brown, as are the upper parts, innermost coverts having a bluish-black shine similar to the male in *cristatus*.

Secondaries   Dark brown.

Tail   Upper tail coverts are bronzy-green barred with light buff. The tail itself is blackish-brown barred with white.

CHICKS

The chicks are similar to the young of *cristatus* but, from the age of four weeks, are more heavily barred.

THE CONGO PEAFOWL
(Afropavo congensis)

This species of peafowl was discovered as recently as 1936 by **Dr. James P. Chapin** from the American Museum of Natural History, New York. His discovery began in 1913 when he noticed a feather, unknown to him, in the hat of a native in the Ituri Forest region on the Congo in West Africa.

It was not until twenty-three years later, however, that he located the source of the feather on the discovery of a pair of stuffed Congo peafowl in the Belgian Congo Museum at Tervueren, Belgium. These birds had been wrongly labelled as young specimens of *Pavo cristatus*.

In the June of 1937 Dr. Chapin set off on an expedition to the Congo in order to gather some specimens of the new species. Several were seen and shot as specimens and this previously undiscovered bird was named *Afropavo congensis* — the Congo peafowl.

A certain number were imported to Europe and America, but there are now only a few pairs to be found in captivity in certain Zoological Gardens and aviaries.

These birds are smaller in size than the Asiatic species and are also of a markedly different appearance, as will be noted from the description below.

Natural Distribution: The tropical forests of the African Congo.

MALE

Crown Black with a crest composed of white and black, hair-like feathers.

Head Velvety black with the bare facial skin being grey in colour.

Neck Throat and upper parts of the neck being bare of feathers and bright red in colour. The lower neck having feathers which are violet in colour and may also be bright blue.

Breast Upper breast also violet, changing to a blackish-blue and then a dark green on the lower parts.

Belly Dull black.

Thighs Dark green, being lighter at the edge.

Back and **Shoulders** Dark green-brown changing to dark green.

Wing Coverts Green changing to a bluish-lilac.

Tertiaries Black with a broad, dark blue border.

Secondaries Black with a slight blue fringe on the outer web.

Primaries Blackish-brown.

Tail Upper tail coverts dark green-brown changing to green. Retrices are black with a broad disintegrated bluish-lilac band at their tip. The male lacks the massive and colourful train of both the green and blue species of peafowl and also has a different cry.

Bill and **Legs** Grey.

Total Length 67 cm (26.4 inches)

Wing 32 cm (12.6 inches)

Tail 30 cm (11.8 inches)

FEMALE

Crest Smaller than that of the male and brown in colour; lacking the black and white colouring.

Head Light brown with the same bare red patch as the male.

Breast Light brown with a darker barring on the lower parts.

Belly Dull black.

Thighs Chestnut with brown barring.

Back and Shoulders Glossy green, each feather being brown with a 'V' shaped, pale buff bar and a broad green fringe.

Wing Coverts Having the same feather pattern and colour as the shoulders and back.

Tertiaries Glossy green barred with buff as in the shoulders.

Secondaries Brown, boldly barred with blackish-brown.

Primaries Brown.

Tail Upper tail coverts have the same feather formation as scapulars and wing coverts. Retrices are brown, boldly barred with blackish-brown. Tips of feathers are metallic green.

Bill and Legs Grey.   **Wing** 28 cm (11 inches).

Total Length 60 cm (23.6 inches).   **Tail** 22 cm (8.7 inches).

CHICKS

The young of the Congo peafowl are very handsome and unlike any other game-bird in colour.

The cheeks, throat and underparts are a buffy-yellow, whilst the head, ear coverts and back remain a blackish-brown. The wings and their coverts are basically brown; the larger coverts having a light band and the secondaries being broadly barred with black. The tail is dark brown.

MORE ABOUT HYBRIDS

The Pied and Spalding peafowl have already been mentioned as being hybrids formed from a cross between two different species of *Pavo*. Although very rare, the author feels that the incidence of a hybrid resulting from a cross between a peafowl and another member of the gallinaceous group of birds must be mentioned.

For twenty years the Bronx Zoo in New York kept a hybrid bird produced from the mating of a Blue Indian peacock with a domestic Guinea hen. The bird produced was sterile and had the appearance of a young peafowl in its first year. The upper parts were mostly barred, with the neck being a dark bluish-lilac in colour; the lower breast was blackish-green. The tail, in formation, was similar to that of a peahen, having elongated tail coverts. There was an absence of any crown or crest.

A further hybrid of this kind was bred by a Mr. Wheadon of Ilminster, from a cinnamon and white domestic fowl and a Black-winged peacock. The resulting hybrid had the basic shape of a peahen but lacked the crest or crown. Much of the facial skin was bare and the predominant colour of the plumage was white, mottled and irregularly barred with dark brown-black. (See Figure 3.4)

Figure 3.4 Black-winged Peacock × Domestic Fowl

IV

Management of
Peafowl

Figure 4.1 Peafowl may be allowed to roam in a large garden or park
Top: Green Peafowl
Middle: Congo Peafowl
Bottom: Black-winged Peafowl

Management of Peafowl

BEFORE examining the requirements for keeping peafowl in complete domestication, it is advisable to look at the type of bird that is to be dealt with in relation to its natural environment. Remember that peafowl are tall birds and that the male has a spreading train which takes up considerable space.

NATURAL LIVING HABITS

Peafowl live off the countryside, their food consisting of corn, berries and insects. Their habits and diet have been summed up by Oliver Goldsmith (*A History of the Earth and Animated Nature*) as follows:

> "Like other birds of the poultry kind the peacock feeds upon corn, but its chief predilection is for barley. But as it is a very proud and fickle bird, there is scarcely any food that it will not at times covet and pursue. Insects and tender plants are often eagerly sought at a time that it has a sufficiency of its natural food provided more nearly. In the indulgence of these capricious pursuits walls cannot easily confine it; it strips the tops of houses of their tiles or thatch, it lays waste the labours of the gardener, roots up his choicest seeds, and nips his favourite flowers in the bud. Thus its beauty but ill recompenses for the mischief it occasions; and many of the more homely looking fowls are very deservedly preferred before it."

They are strong and vigorous birds and need little attention. Indeed, provided there are no predators such as foxes in the vicinity, they thrive best when left to roam freely. As Lewis Wright observed (*ibid*), peafowl "must be left in great degree to manage themselves". Nevertheless, the bird fancier may wish to know how to keep birds with limited space available. However, it must be remembered that peafowl should never be kept in *very limited* space. They are large, active birds who need sufficient space in which to turn and exercise.

Nor should they be kept in close proximity to other domesticated birds. They can inflict considerable pain and damage to fowl such as poultry and ducks. Obviously, an adult peafowl can kill poultry chicks and will do so without any apparent twinge of conscience.

Peafowl can also be quite noisy, a screeching call being quite normal. This is another reason for not confining them to a relatively small garden or yard. Even so they can become extremely tame and domesticated.

To provide a guide to the bird fancier who wishes to begin keeping peafowl, the author feels that it would be as well to use, as an example, his own methods and ideas on caring and managing the birds. Common sense must play a great part in the keeping of all animals and birds but, nevertheless, there are certain rules and guides which are best followed.

51

It is these which the author has set down below, using his own birds as an example.

HOUSING

THE SHED

For many years the author has kept a pair of Spalding peafowl in a large wooden shed measuring 3 × 2.5 m which is 1.80 m high.

At the front of this shed there is a large door, a window and, beneath this, a smaller sash door measuring 50 × 40 cm. This smaller door moves along a rail which is mounted on the innerside of the shed itself and is moved by means of a wooden handle attached to the outside.

From the centre of one side wall to the other a pole or section of branch is mounted which is some 8 to 10 cm thick. This provides a rounded perch for the birds which should be placed approximately 80 cm above the ground.

Insulation

The shed itself is constructed entirely of wooden boards, these being completely painted to seal them against the damp and cold. The author uses a green coloured paint but other colours may be employed and, where appropriate, creosote may be quite suitable.

In order to insulate the roof and prevent the entry of rain and draughts the use of material other than, or additional to, wood is essential. Corrugated asbestos, corrugated iron and roofing felt are all available, but the author feels that there are certain advantages to the first which render it more suitable for the purpose than the other two. If handled carefully, corrugated asbestos is easy to use as roofing material and does not rust like corrugated iron or tear like felt. Furthermore, it does supply quite good insulation which may be improved by the use of an inner lining of hardboard. Between this and the asbestos it is advisable to sandwich a further layer of insulating material, thus keeping the shed cool in summer and warm in winter.

The shed should be set on bricks, two being set under each of the four corners, as is the author's own aviary. This avoids dampness to the floor and discourages rats and other vermin from burrowing through the ground, which would otherwise be directly beneath the shed, and possibly gaining entry. The floor of the shed should be covered with a layer of peat-litter, some 10 to 15 cm thick. Other suitable bedding materials are wood shavings, leaves and sand. Any of these will provide the peafowl with a warm floor on which they may lie in relative comfort.

Scaled and Congo peafowl require a well insulated house in the cold winter months, giving a temperature of some 15°C (59°F).

Other domestic birds

Occasionally, peafowl may be kept with other fowl if the house available is solid and of adequate size. However, they are best kept by themselves and should never be kept with ducks, geese or turkeys. This would

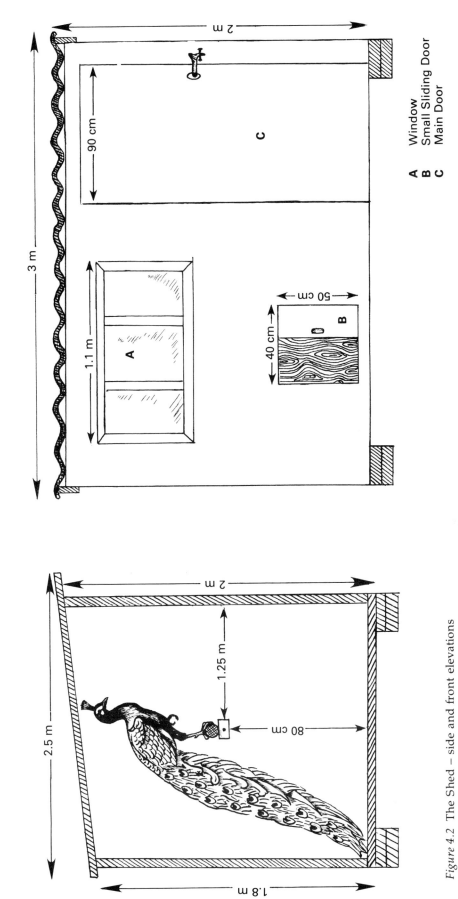

Figure 4.2 The Shed – side and front elevations

Note the measurements of the shed which allow the birds to turn easily. As can be seen from the diagram, the importance of space is the main consideration when building or buying a shed. A perch should be available to the birds and the shed should be well-insulated and vermin-proof.

A Window
B Small Sliding Door
C Main Door

result in fighting between the birds and subsequent damage to plumage and, possibly, to the health of the birds. In the breeding season the peahen should always be separated from other domestic birds even if they appear to be the best of friends.

The breeding place

The peahen prefers to make her nest in a mound of dry hay, leaves or straw, or in a similar mound made from dry earth and sand, covered with grass or leaves. The breeding place must be dry and free from draughts in order that the peahen is able to incubate her eggs in comfort; any distractions may cause her to desert the nest.

Cleanliness

The shed and aviary should be cleaned out regularly, as should the surrounding area, especially if other domestic animals are kept. The manure or dung of animals such as cows or pigs emits noxious gases and is also a prime source of parasites which are detrimental to the health of the birds. All vessels for food and water should also be cleaned regularly. Food which becomes fouled by the birds or by mildew, fermentation or by simply becoming "sour", should be removed instantly as it will undoubtedly cause illness among the birds.

THE PARK

Several fully grown peafowl— cocks and hens together— may be kept in a large enclosed garden or park and left to roam free. If an area of land such as this is not available then each pair of birds should be kept in a large aviary, separated from the others. This aviary should be at least 5 to 6 m in length and should have an adequate shed, as described in the previous section, for the birds to use for shelter.

THE AVIARY

Enclosing the shed and the surrounding area there should be an aviary which provides the birds with adequate room to move about in the open air, without the danger of predators. To prevent the entry of such animals as foxes, cats and dogs, the aviary should be constructed of substantial wire-netting, at least 2 m in height, which should be mounted on iron stakes. These should be bedded into the ground with the use of cement. To avoid rusting the author uses wire-netting which is covered with a layer of green plastic, but this does have the disadvantage of being more expensive. The iron stakes themselves should be covered with a special rust-resistant paint.

The roof of the aviary should be constructed of closely meshed wire-netting to prevent the entry of predators and also to keep the birds from escaping. The wire-netting forming the walls of the aviary should be entrenched into the ground to a depth of 10 to 15 cm to prevent the intrusion of vermin such as rats, mice and other rodents, which otherwise may gain entry by burrowing under the wire.

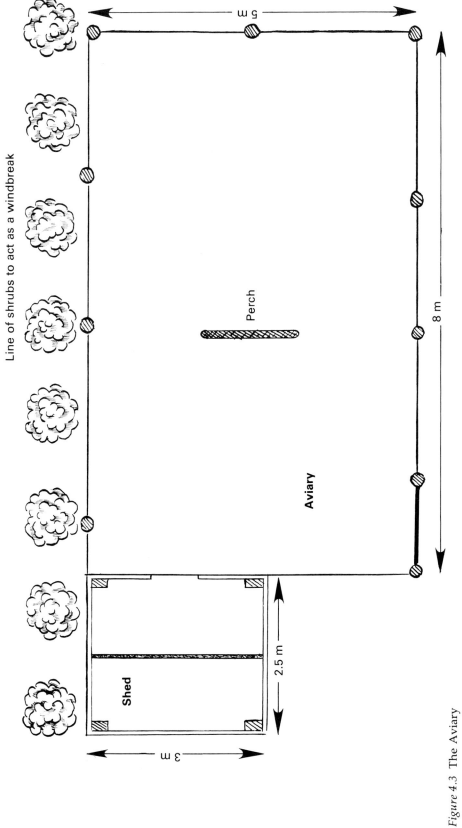

Line of shrubs to act as a windbreak

5 m

8 m

Perch

Aviary

Shed

3 m

2.5 m

Figure 4.3 The Aviary

The aviary must be large enough to accommodate the peafowl in comfort. A wire-netting roof is an essential feature as it acts as a deterrent to predators. Shelter, in the form of shrubs or bushes, should be provided against the wind.

Inside the aviary there should be a plentiful supply of fresh, green grass available to the birds, but the author has found it best to remove any shrubs or bushes to prevent damage to the train of the male peafowl.

In the middle of his aviary, however, the author has mounted a branch, some 10 cm thick and approximately 1.3 m long. This perch for the birds is some 60 cm above the ground and the birds use it as a popular perching place, especially in fine weather.

Along one side of the aviary, and placed approximately 1 m from the outside edge of the wire, the author has planted a row of red-currant bushes. These form a shelter for the birds against the wind, for, whilst peafowl are quite hardy, it is advisable to erect windbreaks and create sun traps wherever possible. Peafowl look magnificent when seen in the sunlight and if this aspect can be combined with overhanging bushes or trees, situated outside the aviary, to provide shade when required, then the birds will thrive all the more.

FEEDING

The author feeds his peafowl mainly on the normal feed given to poultry, consisting of a mixture of different grains: maize, rye, barley and wheat. Limestone and oyster shell grit should also be added to the feed.

The food is thrown into the aviary at most times of the year so that the birds are forced to exercise by scratching about on the ground for the grain. However, if there is much snow on the ground in the winter, the grain mixture should be placed in a trough situated inside the shed. Each bird should be given two handfuls in the morning and this feed then repeated in the afternoon.

It is important to vary the diet of the birds in order that they may not lose interest in their food. For this reason a change from their normal grain mixture may be achieved by substituting cooked potatoes, rice, carrots and peas for part of the grain diet. Salad vegetables may also be used in this way, as well as cabbage and fruits.

Peafowl are lovers of grass so this must be present in the aviary in sufficient quantities along with dandelions and other palatable weeds which serve as a further supplement to their normal diet. In winter, when these weeds and grasses may be scarce, it will be found that the birds like to eat the dried leaves of fruit trees and bushes; these should then be made available.

Peafowl must have clear, fresh drinking water at all times. This should be renewed several times a week, especially in the summer months. In the winter warm water should be provided and a check made to ensure that this does not become frozen. If snow is lying on the ground then the provision of water is not as essential, but a drink is always welcome.

The practice outlined above is followed by the author, but variations are possible. Some breeders treat peafowl exactly like other domesticated fowl and keep hoppers within the shed, allowing the birds to run in an orchard or paddock.

Growers' pellets may be used for young stock, whereas layers' pellets would be fed when dealing with fully grown stock. A grit hopper may also be provided, duly topped up.

BREEDING AND REARING

As the weather gets warmer the peahen begins preparation to lay her eggs. These are usually laid in May but, if the weather is cool, may be laid as late as June. The number of eggs laid varies, but as a general guide it may be as well to recount the story of one of the author's peahens.

Recently, in June, the author's Spalding peahen laid a clutch of twenty-five eggs in the corner of the shed on a layer of peat-litter which served as her nest. The first batch consisted of fourteen eggs, but these were rejected by the bird and no effort was made to incubate them. The reason for this rejection could have been the fact that there were too many eggs for one bird to cover and so the author took them from the hen and gave them to a pheasantry.

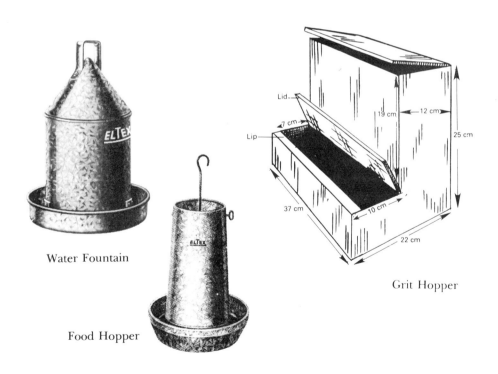

Water Fountain

Food Hopper

Grit Hopper

Figure 4.4 Feeding Utensils
Note: Keep under cover or water will get into the hopper and make it rather 'sour'

Plate 9 Accommodation

       Top: Inside the Shed

     Bottom: The Aviary

Room is necessary both inside the shed and outside, in the aviary. Cramped conditions may result in damage to the plumage of the birds, especially to the extensive train of the male.

Plate 10 Stages of growth in the young birds

Top Left: Spalding chick – one week old
Top Right: Spalding hen with young of three months
Bottom Left: Green peacock showing second year plumage
Bottom Right: Young Blue peafowl at three months

The peahen then proceeded to lay an additional eleven eggs which she incubated. Five of these hatched out after twenty-eight days and the chicks were soon to be seen following their mother, catching small insects and stripping grass seeds from the turf.

FEEDING THE YOUNG

During the first six weeks after hatching the author fed the young of the Spalding peahen on a mixture of commercial pheasant chick crumbs and a special food which consisted of dried insects, ground rusk and protein supplement. To this the author added finely minced hard-boiled egg, soaked rusk, milk and small pieces of parsley.

This mixture should be served in a crumbly state, but should be neither too wet nor too dry. The author puts this food on a flat plate and later, as the chicks grow, in a shallow bowl.

From the third week small seeds such as broken groats, hemp seed and millet seed should be added to the mixture. These are obtainable from most pet shops and are usually used for feeding parrots and other cage birds. Additional pheasant grain food, consisting of larger seeds and corn should be supplied from the sixth week onwards.

After three months the young should accept the normal food given to their parents — poultry food and grain, together with supplements.

MANAGEMENT DURING REARING

The peacock must be separated from both the chicks and the peahen when being fed, otherwise the male may try to eat the special food intended for the young. The best way of achieving this separation is to entice the mother and her young into the shed and then close the door behind them. They may then be given their food inside the shed whilst the peacock remains in the aviary itself.

To prevent any ill-feeling between the birds, the male may be given some soaked rusks as a supplement to his normal feed. This usually stops the peacock from becoming aggressive towards the chicks.

Sometimes one of the young chicks may be bullied by its parents or by the other youngsters. This may then cause it to go off its food and pine away. When this happens it is necessary to take care of this specimen separately, returning it to the family only after some weeks.

If the weather takes a turn for the worst and it begins to rain heavily, then the hen and her chicks must be kept under cover. The young are very sensitive to the wet, cold and damp during the first three months of their lives. Obviously, an occasional shower will not harm them, but they cannot tolerate mud and constant rain. The chicks must also be kept in the shed during the night.

INSECTICIDES

The utmost care must be exercised where the use of chemicals is concern-
ed. One year all the eggs of the author's Emerald peahen were infertile.
The cause for this sudden infertility was found to be that the hen and
cock had picked leaves from the red-currant bushes lining one wall of the
aviary, which had been sprayed with an insecticide to rid them of some
insect pests. The following year the author did not spray the bushes and
most of the eggs were fertile, as is usually the case. Obviously, the
fertility of the birds can be affected by chemicals.

TRANSPORT AND SELLING

Peafowl may be transported for short distances in a large, clean sack with
the top tied. For long distances, however, they should be placed in a
solid, large cardboard or wooden box. Irrespective of the method used,
provision must be made, in the form of holes, so that the birds may get
plenty of fresh air on their journey.

   If the birds are to be sent by train they should be packed in a large
enough box to allow them to rest in comfort. August is a favourable time
to transport adult peacocks as they will be moulting their trains.

PRICES

The prices for which peafowl may be sold vary considerably. A pair of
mature Blue peafowl may often be priced at £50, whilst Pied adult

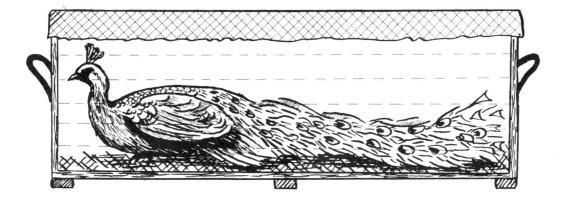

Figure 4.5 Trasportation. Peafowl may be transported in a large box.

peafowl may sell for as much as £100. Spalding birds are generally priced at around £150 with *Pavo muticus muticus* fetching up to £400 for a pair. Single birds sell for around half the prices quoted above.

Young Blue peafowl are often obtainable for around £20 a pair; Spalding for £15 and *muticus* for £250. Yearling birds are usually sold for the same prices as birds of only six months.

Prices for peafowl vary greatly from one country to another. Moreover, much depends on the rarity of a species — the price for a pair of Congo peafowl may be £1,000 or more because these birds are virtually unobtainable.

ILLNESS AND DISEASE

If your birds are on view to the general public or even allowed to roam free in an orchard or paddock, care must be taken against vandals or poachers who may try to harm them in some way, or even to shoot them. For this reason the aviary should be soundly constructed and, if valuable birds are kept, some form of guard dog is usually a sensible idea as long as the birds themselves are not disturbed.

CATCHING THE BIRDS

If, for any reason, one of your birds needs to be caught, the correct method must be used. The bird should be grasped around the shoulders (over the wings) and not by the neck, legs or feet. There is a danger that these parts of the body could be easily broken so care should always be exercised.

FRACTURES

The author's Spalding cock once broke his metatarsal bone. The author made a splint using a short elder stem and then set the foot in a dressing of Plaster of Paris and bandages. This was kept on for three months and then the dressing removed with great care. The foot had mended well and the bird suffered no ill effects from being so long incapacitated.

Fractures of this kind may be set in the manner laid out above but more serious breaks should be left to a qualified veterinary surgeon.

It is not advisable to keep pigeons or doves with peafowl. They may be attracted into a pigeon loft by the food and thereby become injured from being in such a cramped place. Even if no serious injury results there is certain to be damage to the plumage, especially to the train of the male.

Peafowl must never be given meat as a part of their diet. If this is done it will, in time, lead to feather-plucking which is a most vicious habit—the birds will be seen pulling out one another's feathers and even drawing blood. This is detrimental not only to their plumage but also to

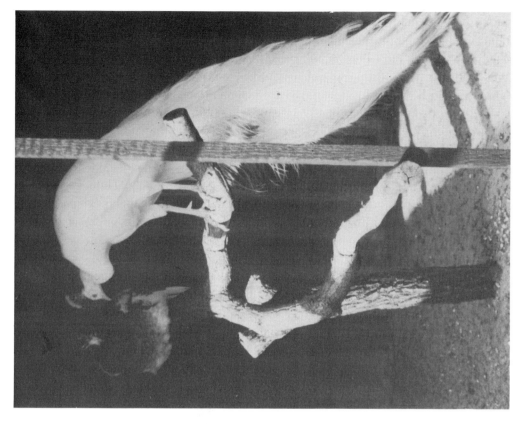

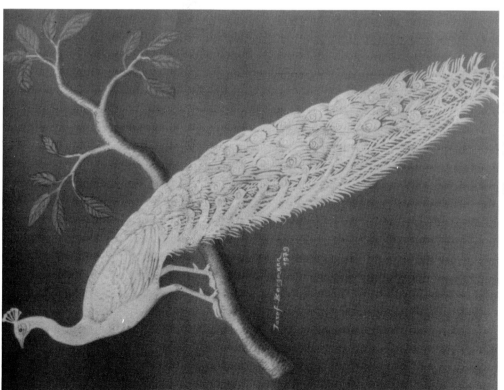

Figure 4.6 Health and Happiness

In their natural surroundings, peafowl are often to be seen perching on the branches of trees.
This situation can be simulated in both the aviary and shed by providing a perch for the birds.
In simulating natural conditions both the health and happiness of the birds can be safeguarded.

their general health and temperament.

Remedies for colds and coughs are available in many forms from pet or bird shops. Some are produced in a form so that they may be mixed or added to the drinking water whilst others may be added to the food. However, in all cases prevention is better than cure and if the birds have an adequate and balanced diet, a clean aviary — free from damp, draughts and vermin— then the probability of them contracting disease is lessened dramatically. When cared for in the proper manner peafowl may live for twenty years or even longer.

Many of the minor illnesses may be dealt with by the use of readily available medicines or simply common sense. However, for more serious complaints such as coccidiosis and similar disorders there are many excellent drugs available on prescription from a veterinarian.

V

Peafowl in
Art*

*This outline has been kept brief, emphasising noteworthy contributions by the artists mentioned. Others could be mentioned as many great artists have included peafowl in their work.

Figure 5.1 Peacocks by Melchior d'Hondecoeter
(*Courtesy:* The Metropolitan Museum of Art; gift of Samuel H. Kress, 1927)

Peafowl in Art

THE peafowl has long played a part in the spiritual and artistic life of many civilizations and cultures, and they have been used as tokens of wealth and splendour from 900 B.C. onwards. The beauty and extraordinary colour of their plumage, especially that of the male, has attracted many aesthetes — writers and artists alike — whose aim was to convey the splendour of the bird through their artistic skills in painting, writing and illustrating.

In the following pages some of those who succeeded in this aim will be discussed and some of the resulting work shown. These artists came from all corners of the world; from Germany, China, India and France but, although from different cultures, all had one thing in common — a fascination and appreciation for the beauty of nature which, surely, is at its most striking in the displaying peacock.

ARTISTS

Melchior d'Hondecoeter (1636–1695) was the last, and possibly the best, of a family of Dutch painters. He worked mainly at The Hague and in Amsterdam and was noted for his paintings of birds and animals. Usually executed in oils, the theme for much of his work was a farmyard or courtyard filled with a variety of exotic birds and animals. The painting illustrated here (Figure 5.1), entitled *Peacocks*, may be found in the Metropolitan Museum of Art, New York, with whose kind permission it is reproduced here. It was donated to the museum in 1927 by Samuel H. Cress. This painting is typical of Hondecoeter's work and, as can be seen from the plate, a variety of creatures are illustrated.

Hondecoeter learnt much about his chosen profession from his father, Gysbert, and also from his uncle, **Jan Baptist Weenix**, who was another well known artist of the time. Hondecoeter was not alone when being taught by his uncle, for the latter's son, **Jan Weenix** (1640–1719), was a fellow pupil. Unlike his cousin, Weenix turned to still-life for the basic theme of almost all his paintings and although animals and birds were a major part of his work they were mostly included in the form of dead game.

The painting shown here is entitled *Dead Birds* and may be found in the Munich Art Gallery. Both artists paid great attention to detail, although their paintings are markedly different in approach, and made efforts to

Figure 5.2 Dead Birds by Jan Weenix
(Courtesy: Munich Art Gallery)

paint the birds as they appeared without exaggeration.

There were many other Old Masters who turned to Nature and her wild creatures to find inspiration for their work. **Frans Snyders** (1579–1657) was one of the latter and, during his lifetime, he produced a large volume of work including many paintings of hunting scenes, animals and birds.

His artistic career began under the guidance of **Pieter Bruegel the Younger** whose pupil he remained for some years. After travelling throughout Italy he settled in Antwerp and was frequently employed by the great **Rubens** to execute the still-life, animal and bird content of his pictures.

Besides working for other great artists of the time Snyders produced much of his own account. The painting shown here (Figure 5.3) demonstrates his skill at reproducing fine detail and also illustrates his extensive knowledge and study of bird life. Countless breeds and varieties are included and, of course, among them stands a majestic Blue peacock.

Rembrandt van Ryn (1606–69) remains an artist known to us all. His paintings and etchings are to be found in all corners of the world and are widely sought after by collectors who will pay, perhaps, thousands of pounds for one small etching. His paintings and drawings cover a wide range of subjects — painted in his inimitable style — and many of these are famous in their own right.

We are indeed fortunate that this great artist may be mentioned here and his work included, for he, like many others, also used the peafowl as

Figure 5.3 Collection of Birds by Frans Snyders

Figure 5.4 The Peacocks by Rembrandt van Ryn
(*Courtesy:* The Rijksmuseum, Amsterdam)

Figure 5.5 The Poultry House by Carl Jutz

Plate 11 *Pair of Peafowl* **by the Japanese artist Maruyama Okyo**

Plate 12 *Green Peacock* **by Araki Kampo**

a subject through which to express his artistic talents.

The painting illustrated in Figure 5.4, entitled *The Peacocks*, may be found in the Rijks Museum in Amsterdam along with further examples of this man's genius as an artist.

Another artist who is known for his paintings of birds, especially poultry and other domesticated fowl, was **Carl Jutz the Elder** (1838–1916). For many years this German artist worked and painted in Dusseldorf. The etching shown here, entitled *Hühnerhof* meaning *The Poultry House*, is dated at around 1878 and shows a Blue peacock with poultry.

Jakob Bogdani (c. 1720) was yet another famous bird artist who often included peafowl in his paintings. Several of these are in the possession of H.M. the Queen, and one of the finest—*Birds in a Landscape*—shows a majestic Pied peacock.

CHINESE AND JAPANESE ART

In both Chinese and Japanese art the peafowl was often used as a symbol of power and, therefore, associated with the powerful figures in their culture and religion. For this same reason it was a popular subject for many of their paintings.

Maruyama Okyo (1733–1795) often painted peafowl and, as can be seen from the painting illustrated here (Plate 11), his portrayal of the birds is markedly different from that of the artists previously discussed. The bird is represented here in a stylized form typical of the approach used by many artists of this country and this is even more pronounced in Plate 12. The latter painting of a Green peafowl by **Araki Kampo** (1831 –1915) from Japan, portrays the peafowl in an exaggerated form to em-phasize the beauty of the plumage and the majestic qualities of the bird.

There are many other artists from China and Japan who are not included here but suffice it to say that in the majority of the work the aim of the artist lies in capturing the colour and appearance of the bird together with its importance as a symbol of wealth and power. For this reason many of the birds are exaggerated in certain ways, be it in colour, size or proportions, in order that this aim may be achieved.

BOOK ILLUSTRATORS

Although the peafowl may be found as the subject for many paintings in galleries and museums its most popular use was as a subject for book illustrations. These were not always books on natural history, though there are a large number of these, as the peafowl was often included in illustrations for children's books, fairy tales and volumes of a similar nature.

One of the earliest stories in which the peacock figures is the *Ramayana* — an ancient Indian legend which is thought to be the best tale of the love of creatures ever told. One of the prominent figures in this tale is

Kartikiya, the War God and son of the Great Goddess. Each character in the story has an attachment to a bird or animal in the world of living creatures and Kartikiya's constant companion is a Blue peacock. The earliest illustrations to the story may be found carved into the walls of temples and ancient buildings around India and the peacock is often portrayed carrying Kartikiya on his back.

PEAFOWL IN BOOKS

It was not until the eighteenth and nineteenth centuries that the peafowl began to figure frequently in natural history books. One of the first illustrations of the peafowl appeared in Brisson's *Ornithologia* published in Paris in 1760. The artist responsible was one **F.N. Martinet** and his fine drawing was of a displaying peacock. This same drawing appeared some years later in a large folio edition of Buffon's *Histoire Naturelle des Oiseaux* as a hand coloured plate. The earlier edition of the latter book contained etchings by **W.H. Freeman**. His etching of *Le Paon* is shown in Figure 5.6.

The 1800s saw an upsurge in the number of books of this kind as an interest in nature, her creatures and her history became more widespread.

Many British publications of this period were illustrated by fine artists and two of the finest early works which include the peafowl must be *The Gardens and Menagerie of the Zoological Society* (1831) and Steward's *Naturalist's Library*.

Perhaps the first bird artist to make a name as an illustrator of natural history books was a Frenchman, **Edouard Travies**. He worked mainly in France and was employed by such people as Cuvier for *Le Régne Animal* (1836–49) and for Orbigny's *Histoire Naturelle* (c. 1840). The illustration shown here by Travies (Figure 5.7) is of a Blue peacock and is a typical example of the fine etchings that were being produced at that time.

Figure 5.6 Le Paon by W.H. Freeman

Plate 13 *Peafowl* **by Ludwig Reichenbach**
Left: Pair of Green Peafowl
Right: Family of Blue Peafowl

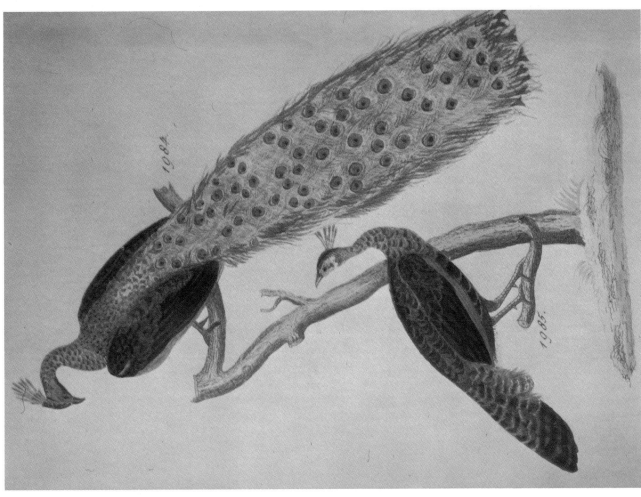

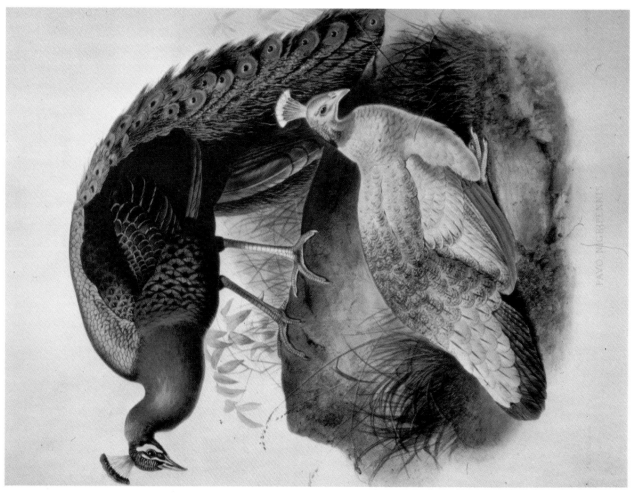

Plate 14 *Peafowl* **by Joseph Wolf**
       Left: Black-winged Peafowl
      Right: Green Peafowl

Figure 5.7 Le Paon by Edouard Travies

Among the most popular of the nineteenth century book illustrators is **Ludwig Reichenbach**. The work of this German artist is widely sought after and now fetches a high price. Between 1845 and 1862 Reichenbach worked in Dresden and Leipzig preparing illustrations for a text that was to span several volumes. The work was published under the title *Die vollständige Naturgeschichte der Vögel des In- und Auslandes* and is filled with over a thousand hand-coloured plates of various birds.

The two illustrations included here are from the above work and are a fine example of Reichenbach's style. Plate 13 shows a pair of Green peafowl on the left, whilst on the right is of a family of Common (Blue) peafowl, illustrating the plumage of the young besides that of the adults.

Another very popular bird artist of this time was **Joseph Wolf** (1820–1900) who contributed his work to a great many volumes. Born in a village near the Rhine river he later moved to England where he developed his artistic skills further and had little difficulty in finding employment as an illustrator.

In 1862 I.G. Wood published Volume II of his *Illustrated Natural History* as the British counterpart to *Brehms Tierleben* which had been published in Germany. Wolf contributed much to this work along with many other illustrators. Figure 5.8 shows an engraving of peafowl beautifully executed by **T.W. Wood**, an English artist, which appeared in this volume alongside the work of Wolf. The author considers it to be one of the finest pictures of its time, even though the artist is relatively unknown.

Wolf went on to work with John Gould and D.G. Elliot for the latter's *Monograph of the Phasianidae or Family of Pheasants* which was eventually published in 1872. Wolf was responsible for the majority of the plates in both the volumes of this work, and two of his illustrations are included here. Plate 14 (left) is entitled *Pavo nigripennis* (the Black-winged peafowl) whilst the illustration on the right shows a pair of Green peafowl. Both are beautifully painted with great attention being paid to the colour and pattern of the feathers, whilst at the same time they portray a realistic picture of the birds in terms of shape and size.

An artist of the early twentieth century who must be mentioned is **Charles Richard Knight** who became known for his paintings and drawings of birds. These first appeared in William Beebe's *Monograph of the Pheasants* (1918–22) which was published in four volumes. Unfortunately, no original is available for inclusion in this book.

This section is completed with one very gifted artist, **Edward J. Detmold** (born 1883). Like his twin brother Maurice, he specialized in drawing and painting birds, animals and fish and both brothers were highly skilled in their work. Much of Edward's work is to be found in story, rather than natural history, books. He illustrated such works as *Aesop's Fables* and *The Arabian Nights* as well as many other children's books that had a natural history theme.

Although his brother committed suicide in 1908 Edward carried on with his work and produced some of his finest illustrations in the years

Figure 5.8 Group of Blue Peafowl by T.W. Wood

Figure 5.9 Green Peacock by Edward J. Detmold

Plate 15 Peacock in Sèvres porcelain made for Ludwig II

Plate 16 Porcelain Peacock designed by Theodor Kärner

before his own suicide in 1957.

The illustration included here (Figure 5.9) was painted for the original edition of Rudyard Kipling's *Jungle Book* (c.1900) and is of a very decorative Green peacock. Detmold managed to convey in his work, perhaps better than most, the true wonder and sense of awe that one feels when confronted with these birds and the author feels that, for this reason, he should be more widely acclaimed.

THE ART NOUVEAU PERIOD

The peacock motif was particularly popular with the craftsmen and artists of the Art Nouveau period because of its versatility as a decorative figure. It was not only the exaggerated plumage that attracted the aesthetes of the time, for the striking, iridescent colours, especially those of the 'eyes', were used as motifs in themselves to decorate material, wallpaper and countless other objects.

There are many examples that could be included in this section, too many to show them all. Therefore, the two artists, or rather craftsmen, that follow have been chosen from the many who used the image of the peafowl in their work.

The first artist to be discussed is **W.J. Neatby** who was a part of the Art Nouveau movement in the area of furniture design and ceramic decorations. His ceramic wall tiles were to be seen in the meat, fish and poultry department at Harrods, London, in 1902. His work had great decorative charm due to his love of birds and animals being given free rein and becoming an essential, and very effective, part of his designs.

The English version of Art Nouveau was very preoccupied with bird and plant life, but in a highly stylized, rather than realistic, form. Peacocks were, obviously, a popular bird, being highly colourful and fantastic and, therefore, without much need of extensive exaggeration.

In Neatby's tiles the stylized approach is evident — two peacocks, highly coloured, are portrayed sitting on the edge of a water fountain in a beautiful park. With their long trains sweeping down around the fountain in almost perfect curves, the design is typical of that period.

A second great craftsman and designer was **Réne Lalique** (1860–1945) who made his name as one of the most famous jewellery designers of the Art Deco/Art Nouveau period. Both the peacock itself, and its plumage, especially the arrangement of the "eyes", figured greatly in his work and designs.

One famous piece illustrating his flair for capturing colour and line is to be seen in his Peacock brooch which may be found in the Musée des Arts Décoratifs in Paris. The main colour scheme used is one of deep blue and gold with emphasis placed on the contrasting colours in the ocelli or "eyes". The beautiful detail on the head and crest of the bird render this piece one of the most delicate to emerge from that time.

Unfortunately, growing pressures in the area of jewellery design turned Lalique towards working with glass. One of his most famous pieces of glass work is a decorative lamp. The body is made from moulded opaline glass, as is the elaborate stopper which is topped with an acid-etched decoration of peacocks on a plastic base. This lamp illustrates, perhaps best of all, his attention to detail, line and form with the formation of the feathers portrayed so beautifully in the glass.

The peafowl motif was not only confined to glass work and jewellery. The image of the peacock was to be found engraved on the glass fronts of show cases, painted on screens and the "eyes" were often incorporated into textile designs.

ORNAMENTS

Although china ornaments of this bird are rare, the author feels that there are two which are worth mention.

The first is to be found at the Linderhof castle of **King Ludwig II**. Ludwig did much towards establishing Munich as a respected art centre through encouraging and patronizing art in its many forms. He had built a series of castles in which he could retire from reality and one of these, Linderhof, built in the years between 1870 and 1886, is a fine example of his love for splendour and colour.

The whole castle is richly decorated, indeed many of the rooms resemble stage sets which could be due to the fact that many were designed by the director of the Munich State Theatre, Franz von Seitz. The castle itself is surrounded by a park complete with a grotto and several highly decorative pavillions.

This Bavarian King commissioned several craftsmen to make models of peacocks with which he decorated his castle. The peacock shown in Plate 15 is made from Sèvres porcelain and is almost life-size.

Another peacock modelled in porcelain was designed by **Theodor Kärner** around 1908. It was made at the Nymphenburg factory in Germany which, at that time, produced some of the finest porcelain pieces that were to emerge from the second half of the eighteenth century. As can be seen from Plate 16 it is surely one of the most elegant figures ever produced with its fine attention to detail and colour.

Index

References to illustrations are in *italics*.

Afropavo congensis, *see*, Congo peafowl
Alexander the Great, 3
    afforded protection to peafowl, 5
Araki Kampo (1831–1915), 78
    Green Peacock, *76*, 78
Art, *see* Glass work; Jewellery; Paintings of
    peafowl; Porcelain peacocks
Art Nouveau period, 92–3
Asiatic peafowl, natural habitat, 15
Aufidius Hurco, first to fatten peafowl for
    food, 5
Aviaries, 54, *55*, 56, 58, *59*
    guarding, 64

Back feathers, description
    of Black-winged peahen, 35
    of Blue peacock, 34
    of Blue peahen, 34
    of Congo peacock, 47
    of Congo peahen, 47
    of Javenese Green peacock, 38
    of Spalding peacock, 44
Bedding materials, 52
Beebe, William
    Monograph of the Pheasants, 85
Belly
    of Black-winged peahen, 35
    of Blue peacock, 29
    of Blue peahen, 34
    of Congo peacock, 47
    of Congo peahen, 47
    of Javenese Green peacock, 38
Bible, references to peafowl, *see*
    Solomon, King of Israel
Bill, *2*
    of Blue peacock, 34
    of Blue peahen, 35
    of Congo peacock, 47
    of Congo peahen, 48
    of Javenese Green peacock, 39
    of White peafowl, 36
Black-winged peafowl (*Pavo cristatus* mut.
    nigripennis) *8*, 29, *32*, *50*
    described by Dr Sclater, 10
    description, 35–6
    feather formation and pattern, *46*
    first appearance in England, 35
    first mentioned by Latham (1823), 4
    hybrid produced with domestic fowl, 48,
        48
        with Pied peafowl, *18*

painted by Joseph Wolf, *82*, 85
    stages in plumage growth, *18*
Blue (Indian) peafowl (*Pavo cristatus*), *8*, 30,
    31
    crossed with domestic Guinea hen, 48
    cry during courtship, 15
    described by Jerdon, 10
    description, 29, 34
    distribution, 29
    feather formation and pattern, *45*
    in Jutz's *The Poultry House*, *73*, 78
    in Snyder's *Collection of Birds*, 71, *71*
    in the *Ramayana*, 79
    in Travies' *Le Paon*, 79
    mentioned by Tegetmeier, 10
    painted by Reichenbach, *81*
    painted by T.W. Wood, 85, *86*
    plumage display at one year old, *18*
    prices, 63
    three-month-old young, *60*
    three-week-old chick, *18*
Bogdani, Jakob (c. 1720)
    Birds in a Landscape, 78
Book illustrations featuring peafowl, 78–9
Breast
    of Black-winged peahen, 35
    of Blue peacock, 29
    of Blue peahen, 34
    of Burmese Green peacock, 44
    of Congo peacock, 47
    of Congo peahen, 47
    of Indo-Chinese peacock, 39
    of Indo-Chinese peahen, 44
    of Javenese Green peacock, 38
    of Spalding peacock, 44
    of Spalding peahen, 46
Breeding, 57
    season in Europe, 15
        in India, 10
Brisson: *Ornithologia* (1760), 79
Bruegal, Pieter, the Younger (c.1564–c.1637),
    71
Buddha, associations of peacock with, 3
Buffon, Georges Louis Leclerc, Comte de
    Histoire Naturelle des Oiseaux, 79
Burmese Green peafowl (*Pavo muticus
    spicifer*)
    description, 44
    distribution, 44

Camphire, 10, 10n
Carvings in temples, 79
Catching technique, 64

Ceramic tiles depicting peafowl, 92
Ceylon, 10
    export of parrots, 11
    peacock-shoots, 22
    prevalence of peafowl, 5
Chapin, James P., 46
China (ceramics), *see* Porcelain peacocks
China (country)
    Asiatic peafowl native to, 15
    Symbolic use of peafowl, 3
    use of peafowl in art forms, 78
Christian symbolism of peacock, 3/4
Coccidiosis, 66
Cold adaptation, 15
Cold and cough remedies, 66
Congo peafowl (*Afropavo congensis*), 29, 42,
    43, *50*
    courtship display, 15, 20
    description, 47–8
    discover in 1937, 5, 46
    distribution, 47
    metallic gloss on plumage, 20
    natural habitat, 15
    prices, 64
    temperature requirements, 52
Courtship display, 10–11, 15–16, *17*, 20, 22
Crest, 2, 24
    of Blue peacock, 29
    of Blue peahen, 34
    of Congo peacock, 47
    of Congo peahen, 47
    of Green peacock, 36
    of Javanese Green peacock, 38
    of Spalding peacock, 44
    of Spalding peahen, 46
Cry, 20, 51
    during courtship ritual, 15, 16
    inconvenience to people, 22
Culmen, length
    in Blue peacock, 34
    in Blue peahen, 35
    in Javanese Green Peacock, 39
Cuvier, Georges Léopold Chrétien Frédéric
    Dagobert, Baron
    La Règne Animal, 79

Detmold, Edward J. (1883–1957), 85
    Green Peacock, *87*, 92
Detmold, Maurice (1883–1908), 85
Diseases, 66
Doves, should not be kept with peafowl, 64

East Indies, origin of peafowl in Europe, 5
Eggs, *25*
    average size of clutch and description, 20,
        25, 57, 62
Elliott, Daniel Giraud
    *Monograph of the Phasianidae or Family of
        Pheasants*, 85
Emerald peafowl, *see* Spalding (Emerald)
    peafowl
Eyes, of White peafowl, 36
"Eyes" (feature of plumage), *see* Ocelli

Feather-picking, 64
Feet, *see* Legs and feet

Fertility, effect of insecticides, 63
The Field
    article on peafowl by "Ornithognomon",
        20, 22
Flight, *21*, 22
    of peachicks, 25
Food
    avoidance of meat in diet, 64
    for young, to three months, 62
    in domestication, 56–7
    in the wild, 11, 15, 20, 51
Forehead, 2
Fractures, treatment of, 64
Francis I, use of preserved peacocks at table
    centrepieces, 10
Freeman, W.H.
    Le Paon, 79, *79*

*The Gardens and Menagerie of the Zoological
    Society* (1831), 4, 79
Glasswork, designs based on peacocks, 93
Goldsmith, Oliver
    A History of the Earth and Animated Nature,
        5, 10
    on habits and diet of peafowl, 51
Gould, John, 85
Grains in feed, 56
Grass, in the aviary, 56
Greece, introduction of peafowl, 3, 5, 10
Green (Scaled) peafowl (*Pavo muticus*), 6, *7*, *8*,
    29, *32*, 40, *41*, *50*
    cry during courtship, 15
    described in 1831, 4
    description, 36, 38
    distribution, 36, 40
    drawing brought back by Marco Polo, 4
    feather formation and pattern, *45*
    mentioned by Tegetmeier, 10
    painted by Araki Kampo, *76*, 78
        by Reichenbach, *81*
        by Wolf, *82*, 85
    second year male plumage, *60*
    temperature requirements, 52
    see also Burmese Green peafowl;
        Indo-Chinese peafowl; Javanese Green
        peafowl
Grit in diet, 56, 57
Guinea hen, used to produce hybrid, 48

Habitat, natural, 10, 15
Head
    of Blackwinged peahen, 35
    of Blue peacock, 29
    of Blue peahen, 34
    of Congo peacock, 47
    of Congo peahen, 47
    of Javanese Green peacock, 38
    of Spalding peacock, 44
A History of the Earth and Animated Nature
    (Goldsmith), 5, 10, 51
Hondecoeter, Melchior d' (1636–1695), 69
    Peacocks, *68*
Hopper for food and grit, 57, *57*
Housing, 52, *53*, 54, *55*, 56, 58, *59*

Hunting
forbidden in some Hindu states of India, 10
see also Shooting peafowl
Hybrids, 48, *48*
Pied/Black-winged, *18*
see also Pied peafowl; Spalding peafowl
Hygiene
as preventive measure, 66
of housing, 54

Illnesses, 64, 66
Illustrated Book of Poultry (Wright), 11–12, 22, 51
India
carvings in temples, 79
peacock-shooting, 22, *23*
peafowl native to, 10
peafowl regarded as sacred, 3, 10
Indian peafowl, *see* Blue (Indian) peafowl
Indo-Chinese Green peafowl (*Pavo muticus imperator*), 29
description, 39, *44*
distribution, 39
Insecticides, effect on fertility, 63
Insulation of housing, 52

Japan
symbolic use of peafowl, 3
use of peafowl in art, 78
Java, prevalence of peafowl, 5
Javanese Green peafowl (*Pavo muticus muticus*), 29
description, 38–9
distribution, 38
prices, 64
Jerdon, 10
Jewellery, designs based on peacocks, 92–3
Juno, peafowl dedicated to, 12
Jutz, Carl, the Elder (1838–1916), 78
The Poultry House, 73, 78

Kärner, Theodor
procelain peacock, *90*, 93
Knight, Charles Richard, 85

Lalique, René (1860–1945), 92
Latham, 4
Legs and feet
of Blue peacock, 34
of Blue peahen, 35
of Congo peacock, 47
of Congo peahen, 48
of Javanese Green peacock, 39
of White peafowl, 36
Length (total)
of Blue peacock, 34,
of Blue peahen, 35
of Congo peacock, 47
of Congo peahen, 48
of Javanese Green peacock, 39
of Javanese Gree peahen, 39
of Spalding peacock, 46
Linderhof castle (Bavaria), 93
Longevity of peafowl, 66
Loral patch, 2

Louis II, King of Bavaria, *see* Ludwig II
Ludwig II, King of Bavaria, 88, 93

Malabar, 11
Management
during rearing, 62
housing, 52, *53*, 54, *55*, 56, 58, *59*
space requirements, 51
Mandibles, 2
see also Culmen (upper mandible)
Mantle, 2
Martinet, F.N., 79
Maruyama Okyo (1733–1795), 78
Pair of Peafowl, 75, 78
Moult, 26
good time to transport adults, 63
of males' trains, 11, 26

Natural history books, 79
Naturalist's Library (Steward), 79
Neatby, W.J., 92
Necho, Pharaoh, 11
Neck
of Black-winged peahen, 35
of Blue peacock, 29
of Blue peahen, 34
of Burmese Green peacock, 44
of Congo peacock, 47
of Indo-Chinese peacock, 39
of Javanese Green peacock, 38
of Javanese Green peahen, 39
of Spalding peacock, 44
of Spalding peahen, 46
Nests, 20, 22
habits described by Tegetmeier, 25
in domestication, 54
Nymphenburg porcelain factory, 93

Ocelli, 2
displayed in courtship ritual, 15
of Blue peafowl, 34
of Javanese Green peacock, 38–9
used in design, 92, 93
Ophir (Biblical region), 11
Orbigny, Alcide Dessalines d'
Histoire Naturelle, 79
"Ornithognomon" (pseudonym)
article in *The Field* on peafowl, 20, 22
Ornithologia (Brisson), 79

Paintings of peafowl, 69–78
Pavo cristatus, *see* Blue (Indian) peafowl
Pavo cristatus mut.*nigripennis*, *see* Black-winged peafowl
Pavo muticus, *see* Green peafowl
Pavo muticus imperator, *see* Indo-Chinese peafowl
Pavo muticus spicifer, *see* Burmese Green peafowl
Peachicks
as food, 11
Blue, three-week-old, *18*
descriptions
Black-winged, 36
Blue, 35
Congo, 48

Javanese Green, 39
Spalding, 46
flight, 25
food, to three months, 62
general characteristics, 25
imitation of courtship display, 15
sex differences, 25
sexes alike initially, 20
stages of growth, *60*
see also Breeding; Rearing
Peafowl
as food, 4, 5, 10
compared with other Gallinaceous birds, *14*
general characteristics, 22, 24
history, 3–5, 10–12
in literature, 4, 10–12
introduction into Europe, 3
preserved and used as table centrepieces, 10
relationships with other poultry, 51, 52, 54
wild state, 20, 22
Pelleted foods, 57
Perches, 52, 56, *65*
Pharoahs, imports of peafowl by, 3
Phoenicians, brought peafowl to Solomon, 3
Pied/Black-winged hybrid, *18*
Pied peafowl, 29, *36*
in Bogdani's *Birds in a Landscape*, 78
prices, 63–4
Pigeons, should not be kept with peafowl, 64
Pliny, 5
Plumage, *2*
colours, 24
feather formation and pattern, *45*
maturity reached in third year, 20, 25
second-year Green peacock, *60*
stages in growth, *18*
see also Back feathers; Breast; Neck;
    Primaties; Retrices; Scapulars;
    Secondaries; Tail; Tertiaries; Train;
    Upper tail coverts; Wing coverts
Polo, Marco, 4
Porcelain peacocks, 93
The Poultry Book (Tegetmeier), 10–11, 25
description of peafowl in wild state, 20, 22
Predators, 20
exclusion from aviaries, 54
Prices for peafowl, 63–64
Primaries, *2*
of Black-winged peahen, 35
of Blue peacock, 34
of Blue peahen, 35
of Congo peacock, 47
of Congo peahen, 47
of Javanese Green peacock, 38

Quills, rattled in courtship display, 15, 16

Ramayana (Hindu epic), 78–9
Rearing, 62
stages of growth, *60*
Reichenbach, Ludwig, 85
paintings of peafowl, *81*, 85
*Die vollständige Naturgeschichte der Vögel des
    In-und Auslandes*, 85

Rembrandt van Ryn (1606–1669), 71
The Peacocks, 72, 78
Retrices, *2*, 24
hidden by train, 16
in mating display by hen, 15
lost at moult, 26
Roman Empire
breeding of peafowl, 10
use of peafowl for feasts, 4
Roosting habits, 4, 20
in India, 10, 20
Rubens, Peter Paul (1577–1640), 71
Running ability of peafowl, 11, 20, 22

Scaled peafowl, *see* Green (Scaled) peafowl
Scapulars, *2*
of Black-winged peacock, 35
of Blue peacock, 34
of Blue peahen, 34
of Burmese Green peacock, 44
of Congo peacock, 47
of Congo peahen, 47
of Indo-Chinese peacock, 39
of Javanese Green peacock, 38
of Javanese Green peahen, 39
Sclater, Dr, 10
Secondaries, *2*
of Black-winged peacock, 35
of Black-winged peahen, 35
of Blue peacock, 34
of Congo peacock, 47
of Congo peahen, 47
of Javanese Green peacock, 38
of Spalding peahen, 46
Seitz, Franz von, 93
Sèvres porcelain peacock, *89*, 93
Shank, *see* Tarsus
Sheds, 52, *53*, 54, 58, *59*
Shooting peafowl, 22, 23
see also Hunting
Shoulders, *see* Scapulars
Snakes, destroyed by peafowl, 11, 15
Snyders, Frans (1579–1657), 71
Collection of Birds, 71
Solomon, King of Israel
imports of peafowl, 3, 5, 10, 12
Space requirements of peafowl, 51
Spalding (Emerald) peafowl, *8*, 29
elements in hybrid, 44
feather formation and pattern, *45*
hen with three month old chicks, *60*
mentioned in 1831, 4
one week old chick, *60*
plumage development in hen, *18*
prices, 64
Spurs, *2*
length in Blue peafowl, 34

Tail
of Black-winged peahen, 36
of Blue peacock, 34
length, 34
of Blue peahen, 35
length, 35
of Congo peacock, 47
length, 47

of Congo peahen, 47
  length, 48
of Javanese Green peacock, 38
  length, 39
of Javanese Green peahen, 39
  length, 39
of Spalding peacock, 46
  length, 46
of Spalding peahen, 46
see also Retrices; Train
Tarsus, 2
  length
    in Blue peacock, 34
    in Blue peahen, 35
    in Green peafowl, 36, 38
    in Javanese Green peacock, 39
    in Javanese Green peahen, 39
Tegetmeier, W.B.
  The Poultry Book, 10–11
    description of peafowl in wild state, 20, 22
    on nesting habits and young, 25
Tennant, Sir Emerson, 22
Tertiaries, 2
  of Blue peacock, 34
  of Congo peacock, 47
  of Congo peahen, 47
  of Javanese Green peacock, 38
Thighs
  of Black-winged peacock, 35
  of Blue peacock, 34
    length, 34
  of Blue peahen, 34
  of Congo peacock, 47
  of Congo peahen, 47
  of Javanese Green peacock, 38
    length, 39
Tigers, often found with peafowl, 22
Train, 2, 24, 24
  in courtship ritual, 15, 16, 17
  moulting, 11, 26
  of Blue peacock, 34
  of Javanese Green peacock, 38–9
  see also Courtship display
Transport arrangements, 63, 63
Travies, Edouard, 79
  Le Paon, 84

Tukiyyim, meaning of Hebrew word, 11–12

Upper tail coverts, 2, 24
  in mating display of hen, 15
  of Blue peafowl, 34
  of Javanese Green peahen, 39

Water requirements, 15, 56
Weenix, Jan (1640–1719)
  Dead Birds, 69, 70
Weenix, Jan Baptist (1621–1660), 69
Western Burmese Green peafowl, 29
Wheadon, Mr (of Ilminster), 48
White peafowl, 29, 37
  description, 36
  management in domesticity, 36
Williamson, Colonel, 22
Wing coverts, 2
  of Black-winged peacock, 35
  of Blue peacock, 34
  of Congo peacock, 47
  of Congo peahen, 47
  of Javanese Green peacock, 38
  of Javanese Green peahen, 39
  of Spalding peacock, 46
  of Spalding peahen, 46
Wings
  feathers lost at moult, 26
  length
    of Blue peacock, 34
    of Blue peahen, 35
    of Congo peacock, 47
    of Congo peahen, 48
    of Javanese Green peacock, 39
    of Javanese Green peahen, 39
Wolf, Joseph (1820–1900), 85
  paintings of peafowl, 82
Wood, I.G.
  Illustrated Natural History, 85
Wood, T.W.
  Group of Blue Peafowl, 85, 86
Wright, Lewis
  Illustrated Book of Poultry, 11–12, 22
  on management of peafowl, 51

Young peafowl, see Peachicks

BIBLIOGRAPHY

The following books are referred to in the text. Details are given where these are available.

Garden and Menagerie of the Zoological Society, London Zoological Society, London (1830–1)
Histoire Naturelle, D. D'Orbigny, Paris (1834).
Histoire Naturelle des Oiseaux, Buffon, Paris (c. 1800).
A History of the Earth and Animated Nature, Oliver Goldsmith, London (1866).
Illustrated Book of Poultry, Lewis Wright, London (1920).
Illustrated Natural History, I.G. Wood, London (1862).
The Jungle Book, Rudyard Kipling, London (1894).
Monograph of the Phasiandae or Family of Pheasants, D.G. Elliot, New York (1872).
Monograph of Pheasants, William Beebe (1918–22)
Naturalist's Library, Steward (c. 1800)
Ornithologia, Mathurin Jaques Brisson, Paris (1760).
The Poultry Book, W.B. Tegetmeier, London (c.1890).
Le Regne Animal, Georges L.C.F.D.B. Cuvier (1836–49)